COUNTDOWN!

COUNTDOWN!
or, How Nigh is the End?

PATRICK MOORE

The
History
Press

Cover: image of 'Full Earth' taken by crew of Apollo 17, courtesy of NASA; image of stopwatch by Onur Döngel

First published 1983
This revised edition published 2009

The History Press
The Mill, Brimscombe Port
Stroud, Gloucestershire, GL5 2QG
www.thehistorypress.co.uk

British Library Cataloguing in Publication Data.
A catalogue record for this book is available from the British Library.

ISBN 978 0 7524 5222 7

Typesetting and origination by The History Press
Printed in Great Britain

Contents

Introduction

Do you remember anything about 31 December 1999? I know what I was doing; I was at my home at Selsey getting ready for my New Year's Eve party. I take little notice of Christmas, because Christmas is a family occasion and I do not have a family, so I give my party on 31 December; 1999 was no exception.

Yet in many parts of the world there was considerable tension. We were saying a goodbye to the old century and welcoming in the new – in fact, the new millennium. People wanted to know whether or not this meant anything special. Of course there were the usual prophets of doom, and they were decidedly vocal. Two thousand years since the beginning of the Christian era, and surely this had to be marked in some way. But just how? All kinds of dire predictions were made. There would be thunderstorms, floods, lights in the sky and celestial manifestations of all kinds. But quite apart from this it was suggested that there might be marked effects upon our everyday existence, because – like it or not – we live in a world ruled largely by computers. They had no trouble in changing over from 1998 to 1999, but 1999 was assumed to be the very end of the millennium, and this could confuse a computer very thoroughly. In particular, aircraft and aircraft controllers do depend now upon their computers, and the were serious warnings that a flight over midnight would be dangerous in the extreme. Many people were alarmed, and bookings were heavily down.

But could there be any truth in this? Looking at the Christian point of view the answer had to be 'no', because whenever Jesus Christ was born it was not the year AD 1, and there was no year 0 – a point to which I will return later. (En passant, there are modern groups which object to the use of BC and AD, and want to replace these with something that has no connection with religion. I recently read a perfectly serious book in which the author referred to an event which took place in the year 1250 ACE. It took me some time to realise that he meant AD 1250.) But though we can forget about this kind of thing, there is something to be said about the possible confusion of computers.

Of course, all these predictions were without foundation, and there were no effects at all. Computers coped very nicely, there were no earthquakes or thunderstorms, and the new millennium glided in quite smoothly. But now, a decade later, it may be interesting to look back and see if there is any possibility that the world will come to an end rather unexpectedly.

A few years ago I was walking along Charing Cross Road, in central London, when I came across a man who was wearing sandwich-boards. Normally I would have paid little attention to him, and I would have assumed that he must have been protesting about something quite mundane, but in fact his message was much more dramatic: 'Sinners Repent. The Hour of Doom is at Hand!' I was tempted to question him, but at that moment he stepped off the kerb and was smartly knocked down by a passing cyclist. Rising to his feet, he drew a deep breath and unloosed a volley of lurid invective. He went on speaking for at least five minutes, saying something different all the time; and had I approached him with a mild query, he would undoubtedly have thrown his sandwich-boards at me. Therefore I considered discretion to be the better part of valour, and went on my way.

Actually, end-of-the-world prophets of this kind are much less common than they used to be, which is perhaps a pity; the world would be a duller place without its Independent Thinkers, as I have called them. But they still exist, and in recent years they have been particularly vocal. As the twentieth century passed into history, myriad dire prophecies failed to materialise, but the doom-mongers were not discouraged. Some of the doomsday prophets are purely religious; others fear that we may be blasted out of space by a collision with a comet, an asteroid or even a passing star; yet others maintain that the end of civilization, if not of the world itself, will be brought about by the evil machinations of alien beings in flying saucers. I cannot pretend to be particularly apprehensive, except of the real possibility that some politician will press the wrong button and spark off a nuclear war which would certainly eliminate the human race. And yet the Earth will not last for ever; nothing in the universe is eternal – perhaps not even the universe itself. Our world came into being because of the Sun, and in the end the Sun will destroy it.

I do not want to sound alarmist. The Sun, fortunately for us, is a steady, well-behaved star, and even though it may have fluctuated sufficiently to produce the various Ice Ages (the last of which ended a mere 10,000 years ago) it is not likely to change much in the foreseeable future; indeed, it will remain much as it is for at least a thousand million years, and probably rather longer, so that there is no immediate need for us to pack our bags and start searching for a planet safer than ours. We have a long respite, and if we refrain from blowing each other up we may well hope to find a solution before the crisis becomes really pressing.

However, end-of-the-world seers are still with us, and some of them are ready to give their reasons in great detail. In this book, I want to look at the various theories and try to decide whether or not they are valid. It is a fascinating subject, and it will take us from the realms of astrology and mysticism right through to pure astronomy. I hope that you will enjoy it – and let me say at once that in my view, at least, you will have ample time to read these pages before anything traumatic happens to the world which is our home. If I am wrong, please accept my apologies in advance.

William Miller – and Others

The year was 1843. A brilliant comet blazed down from the sky, 'shaking its fiery locks'. There was great tension in America, and there were thousands of people who believed that the Last Trump was about to sound. This was the time of the Millerite movement, which led to one of the greatest end-of-the-world scares ever known. It was centred on the United States, though traces of it spread further afield, and were slow to fade away. The whole episode had been sparked off by a New England farmer named William Miller.

Miller was not a scientist; he was a student of the Bible, and he was eccentric. Indeed, it is not too much to say that he was as nutty as a fruitcake; but he had a tremendous following, and he was completely sincere. To him, the Second Coming of Christ was imminent, and he regarded it as his bounden duty to spread the word among his fellow men – in which he succeeded only too well, aided and abetted by a clergyman named Joshua V. Hines, who acted as his publicity agent and who fanned the flames with uncanny skill.

I have started this chapter with William Miller because his crusade of doom was so incredibly successful. Even when the fateful year of 1843 was over, the Millerite movement did not perish abruptly; it petered out slowly, and echoes of it lingered on. However, it is best to deal with matters chronologically, and so let us delve back much further than the nineteenth century to see what we can find out.

I do not propose to say much about ancient religions, because they do not really come into the story, and in any case most of them regarded the Earth as eternal. (The same was true of the gods, with the notable exception of those in Norse mythology; you may remember that in the final battle between the Æsir and the forces of evil, the chief god Odin was unceremoniously swallowed by the wolf Fenrir – which was unfortunate for Odin, and may well have given Fenrir indigestion.) So we really begin with St Augustine, who is always remembered as being the man sent to England to convert the inhabitants to Christianity. In this he had considerable success, starting with King Ethelbert of Kent. To be candid, history has been rather kind to Augustine; he came to England with marked reluctance, and his lack of tact very nearly ruined the entire mission. Still, he made his mark, and he was certainly forceful.

Augustine lived in the sixth and seventh centuries AD, and his meeting with King Ethelbert took place in the year 596. Apparently he believed that the Church would last for 1,000 years but no longer, and this paved the way for the first of the religious end-of-the-world scares. If Christ had been born in AD 1, then presumably the year 1000 would complete the cycle. Druthmar, an English monk, even gave a definite date: 24 March – and the stage was set.

There is an immediate flaw here, because, as we have seen, Christ was certainly born well before AD 1. At that time the most powerful man in the European world was Augustus, ruler of Rome. He was Julius Caesar's great-nephew, and had come to power after ousting Mark Antony, who had been too preoccupied with wooing Cleopatra to give his attention to more pressing matters. Augustus is also memorable for having upset the calendar merely because he wanted August, the month named after his honour, to be as long as Caesar's month, July; this is why we now have two consecutive months with thirty-one days each.

However, the approach of AD 1000 was dreaded in every country to which Christianity had penetrated – and this, of course, included England, though the panics were much greater in Italy, France and what is now Germany.

It was, incidentally, a peculiarly unpleasant time for most people. Warfare was widespread, and in addition Europe was in the grip of one of those plagues which have been prevalent every now and then. Many victims may well have thought that the forthcoming end of the world would be a relief rather than otherwise. The Church did not agree, and much money and effort was spent in erecting new cathedrals and renovating old ones – the basic idea being, presumably, that those who were busy upon such noble projects would be given VIP treatment when the world was no more. The English were having extra problems, since Ethelred the Unready sat upon the throne, and the Danish raids were increasing all the time. Ethelred was completely unprepared for them, and it is permissible to think that he would have been equally unprepared for the end of the world, but the matter was never actually put to the test, because nothing happened. The year 1000 came in, passed by, and expired without any divine manifestations whatsoever. It must have been rather galling for the thousands of Christians, mainly from continental Europe, who had sold up all their possessions in 999 and made haste to Jerusalem, where the Second Coming might logically have been expected.

The fears of AD 1000 were decidedly nebulous, and were based upon a mere timescale rather than anything specific in the Bible. Much later came a Spaniard, St Vincent Ferrer, who was born in or about 1350 and died in 1419. He concluded that the world would last for as many years as there are verses in the Psalms. As there are 2,357 verses, there seemed no reason for apprehension.

To catalogue all the individual prophets who forecast doomsday on purely religious grounds would take a long time, and would be rather tedious, but I cannot resist saying something about Solomon Eccles, partly because he was English and partly because he was so odd by any standards. He seems to have been born in London in 1618, and his early career was conventional enough; he was a talented musician, and when still in his twenties he was making a good living by teaching stringed and keyboard instruments. Later he fell in with the Quakers, and began to have visions which told him quite plainly that the end was nigh. Music, of course, was a pastime of the Devil, so he disposed of all his equipment and became a shoemaker. This in itself would have aroused no comment, but he also disposed of his clothing (or most of it; at first he retained a loincloth to cover the appropriate part of his anatomy) and began to burst in upon religious services, imploring the congregation to take heed and be saved while there was still time. It was hardly surprising that preachers did not take kindly to this sort of interruption, and the usual result was that Eccles was thrown out, metaphorically upon his ear. He was even imprisoned, which apparently troubled him not at all.

His strange career approached its zenith, so far as London was concerned, in the years of plague and fire, 1665 and 1666. No doubt he regarded these events as warnings of the holocaust to come. He even attracted the attention of the great diarist Samuel Pepys, who wrote in 1667: 'One thing extraordinary was, this day a man, a Quaker, came naked through the Hall at Westminster, where all the courtiers assembled, only civilly tied about the loins to avoid scandal, and with a chafing-dish of fire and brimstone up in his head did pass through the Hall at Westminster crying 'Repent! Repent!'

Since the stupid Londoners refused to take him seriously, Eccles decided to venture elsewhere; he went to Scotland, and was arrested again. On his release he made for Ireland, where he regarded even a loincloth as an unnecessary encumbrance. Yet he met with no better fortune, and when he streaked naked into Cork Cathedral during a solemn service, both the Church and the civil authorities were outraged. He was whipped through the streets, and then expelled from the city with stern warnings never to come back.

He did join a Quaker missionary party to the West Indies in 1671, and then went to New England, where he was at once arrested and subsequently banished. Nine years later we find him in Barbados, speaking to gatherings of Negro slaves; the authorities intervened and shipped him back to England, where he died. Eccles did not seem to have selected any particular part of the Bible to bolster up his views. He relied upon his instinct and his visions, which is always a risky thing to do; and though he achieved considerable notoriety, he never mustered a following in the way that William Miller managed to do later.

In London, the next important prophet of doom was the Rev. Dr William Whiston, sometime friend of Newton; but since Whiston's theory involved a comet, I propose to defer its discussion for the moment and pass on to the year 1761, when the city was shaken by a couple of earthquakes. Both were very mild, and there was little damage, though a few chimneys were toppled and the shocks were strong enough to be noticeable. They are relevant here only because they led to a noteworthy panic, due entirely to the ravings of an ex-soldier whose name was William Bell.

It is often thought that earthquakes in England are uncommon, but this is not strictly true; a thousand have been recorded altogether, though only one death has been established – in 1580, when a moderate shock dislodged a stone from Christ Church and deposited it upon the head of a luckless youth who happened to be standing underneath.★ In 1761 the jolts were separated by twenty-eight days, and Bell jumped to the conclusion that after another twenty-eight days there would be something much worse – enough, in fact, to destroy the world. He gave the date as 5 April and, for reasons which remain a total mystery, people believed him. Panic broke out, and spread through wide areas of London. A general exodus began; carts and coaches drew out of the city, and camps sprang up in regions which have now been swamped by the spread of London but were then pleasant villages, such as Highgate and Hampstead. Boats were bought up, and the Thames was crowded, presumably because it was thought that water would be safer than dry land.

Bell became famous; everything he said was magnified out of all proportion and by the time that 5 April came the scene was one of utter chaos. Predictably, the day passed quietly, and there was a sense as much of anti-climax as of relief. Bell's enthusiasm for his cause was not dampened, but the authorities had had more than enough, and the luckless ex-soldier was quietly stored in the nearest asylum, where he died some days later. It was a curious episode in every way, and there was no logic behind it.

I can pause only briefly to mention a lady named Mary Bateman, who achieved fame in 1806 when she announced that one of her hens was making a habit of laying eggs with

★ The most violent English quake ever recorded shook the Colchester area on 22 April 1884, at 9.18 a.m. There were two sharp jolts which damaged over 1,000 buildings, and in the village of Abberton only six chimneys were left intact. I have felt two earthquakes myself, one in Shrewsbury and the other in my home village of Selsey, though on each occasion I admit that I had no idea what they were, and put them down to passing lorries.

Jesus Christ's personal seal upon them; clearly, this meant that the Second Coming and the end of the world were imminent. Unfortunately it was found that the eggs had been skilfully treated by Mary herself, so that Christ was not involved. It was, in fact, a pure confidence trick, and Mrs Bateman's subsequent career was no more creditable; it came to an abrupt end after she had been caught giving two wealthy clients a tasty-looking pudding which had been liberally laced with arsenic.

There was also John Tom, a Cornishman who called himself Sir William Percy Honeywood Courtney, and actually stood twice for Parliament. He fought the Canterbury constituency in 1832 and collected 375 votes, which was 372 more than he managed at his second attempt some years later. Eventually he announced that he was the new Messiah, and that he had been sent to give news of the impending destruction of the Earth. Courtney, too, came to an untimely end after he shot a policeman who had been ordered to break up a mob which he had collected and was leading along the road from London to Dover.

Recently, of course, we have had the great expenses scandal when it was found that the Hounourable Members had been using taxpayers' money in ways that were hardly likely to be of much use to their constituents. One MP claimed money for building an island for his ducks, and another charged a large sum having the moat around his house thoroughly cleaned. A senior cabinet minister actually put in a claim for several pornographic films which her husband enjoyed watching. There was an outcry about all of this, and Honourable Members are hardly likely to be admirers of the *Daily Telegraph*, the newspaper which broke the story. However, let us forget the present crop of dubious MPs, and return to the greatest of all prophets of doom, William Miller.

Judged by any standards, Miller was a phenomenon. His background was quite normal; he was born in Pittsfield,

Massachusetts, and his parents were farmers in a modest way. They were also Baptists, which was admittedly harmless. William's only sign of eccentricity was that he was an avid reader who devoured any book he could find, which was by no means common at the time. When he and his family moved to the state of Vermont, he became known as a young man of learning, and he was elected Constable of the town of Poultney; in 1809 he was even made Sheriff, and clearly he was cast in a different mould from most of his contemporaries. He married and at that stage was by no means of a religious turn of mind. He went so far as to declare that the Bible was nonsense, an attitude which horrified his parents.

Meanwhile, storm clouds were gathering, and war against the English was more than probable. Miller decided to serve his country, and so he joined the army. In 1810 he was commissioned, and by 1812 he held the rank of captain. He saw plenty of action, but he also met with an accident which probably changed the whole course of his life. The exact details of the mishap are unknown, but involved a fall from a cart, and the fact that Miller landed on his head may well have been the root cause of his transformation from an energetic, practical men into a fanatical end-of-the-worlder. We will never know. However, the change was not immediately obvious, and he stayed in the army until 1815, when he resigned his commission and established a farm at Low Hampton, which was then a remote part of New York State.

It was at Low Hampton that Miller found God — or thought he did. His lifestyle changed entirely, and he began to spend more and more time reading the Bible, particularly the Book of Daniel. The walls of his study were festooned with charts and graphs, and he became more or less a recluse. Eventually he decided that the Second Coming of Christ was nearer than most people imagined, and would signal the end of the world as we know it. What of the date? By 1832 he had the answer; the world would be destroyed in 1843, probably at midnight at the spring equinox on 21 March.

At first he was cautious. Should he announce the dread news, or wait until the Earth was snuffed out like a candle flame in the wind? To say nothing might be more merciful. On the other hand, there was plenty of sin around (though no doubt much less than there is today), and it would be only right to give the sinners time to repent so that they could face their Maker with confidence and a bright smile. Moreover, there were other prophets who were giving wrong dates. (One was a certain Harriet Livermore, whose career is decidedly obscure, but who expected the Last Trump to sound sometime in 1847. Another was a Captain Saunders, and yet a third was Joseph Wolff, who lived appropriately in Jerusalem, and who held the same opinion. Wolff expected Christ to appear on top of the Mount of Olives. One of his followers was Lady Hester Stanhope, a niece of William Pitt, who subsequently repaired to the top of the Mount taking two white horses with her – one for Jesus and the other for herself.)

Eventually Miller made up his mind. He must spread the word, and there were only a few years left. In 1832 he began his campaign by preaching in the local church. From all accounts, he was an excellent orator of the Hitler variety, and he was certainly positive. The end was nigh, he thundered; those who had led evil lives must make full atonement before it was too late, or they would be cast down into the flames of hell. It was a depressing prospect.

At first his success was modest. Some of the locals took him seriously, while others dismissed him as a crazy old man. What may have helped him was the meteor shower of 1833 when, for some hours, shooting stars 'rained down like snowflakes', indicating divine displeasure. Nowadays we know that the shower was due to the meteors known as Leonids. Periodically the Earth plunges through the main swarm of tiny particles, scooping up many of them. They are associated with a periodical comet, Tempel–Tuttle, which has an orbital period of thirty-three years. When the comet returns to the neighbourhood of the Sun, we are sometimes treated to the spectacle of a major 'meteor storm', as happened in 1799 and again in 1833.★ To Miller, this was a sign that he was thinking along the right lines.

Gradually his fame spread. Over the following years he preached almost 1,000 sermons, and when challenged by sceptics he was able to give as good as he got; so far as the Bible was concerned he had done his homework extremely well, and of his sincerity there was no doubt at all. The Millerite sect became firmly established, and the year 1843 was awaited with considerable apprehension. It was at this juncture that Miller met up with a man who was destined to play a major role in the whole episode – the Elder Joshua V. Hines, a Baptist who had considerable influence in the city of Boston.

Hines is something of an enigma. While Miller was an honest fanatic, Hines was more of what we might call a con man. He may or may not have believed in the approaching holocaust; on the whole it seems that he didn't, but in any event he decided to appoint himself Miller's business manager. He invited him to preach at the Chardon Street Baptist Chapel in Boston, and hundreds of people turned up. The meeting was an outstanding success, and Miller

★ There was another Leonid 'storm' in 1866. The expected displays of 1899 and 1933 did not materialise, because the orbit of the stream had been perturbed by the gravitational pulls of the planets, but in 1966 the Leonids were back with a vengeance – though the main display on 17 November took place when it was daylight over Europe, and was best seen from America. The comet came back once more in 1998, and a reasonably good display of Leonids was seen.

followed it with more sermons throughout the following week. Hines organised things with consummate skill, and placards and advertisements began to appear, together with the inevitable men wearing sandwich-boards (shades of the Charing Cross Road!). Next came a series of meetings in Portsmouth, New Hampshire, where the results were much the same. The Millerites gained ground every day, and Joshua Hines resigned his official position as preacher in order to devote all his time to the movement. He even founded a paper, *Signs of the Times*, in which the message was given in unmistakable terms. Whether any issues of this periodical survive I do not know; I have been unable to locate any, but during the peak of Millerism it was all the rage.

Even New York was not immune. Wall Street and skyscrapers lay in the future, but plenty of people lived there, and Miller descended upon the city like an east wind, bellowing out his warnings and exhorting all sinners to repent. Whether New York had more than its fair share of sinners is open to question, but at this stage there were many Millerites who had sold all their belongings and joined in the crusade, firmly convinced that the Lord was about to swoop down from above and remove the Earth from the universe together with everybody in it.

Things were not helped by the appearance of a brilliant comet which dominated the night sky and caused a great deal of alarm and despondency. It was now 1843, and the Millerite movement was at its zenith; it did not even matter that William himself was ill with fever and had temporarily withdrawn from the scene. As the spring equinox approached, hysteria took over. On the evening of 21 March there was a great exodus from Boston, presumably because the Lord would be more likely to descend in open country than in a city, with the attendant danger of being impaled upon a chimney stack or something equally inconvenient. Alas, nothing happened, but stirring events were taking place elsewhere. In the town of Westford, Massachusetts, hundreds of Millerites had assembled, and when they heard the sound of a trumpet they were naturally convinced that the end had come at last. Several people fainted before it was discovered that the trumpet call had been given by a local drunk, who had a perverted sense of humour and who had become thoroughly tired of being kept awake at night by the sounds of chanting and praying.

The world was still intact when 22 March dawned. There had been quite a number of casualties, including one man who had attempted a flight to Heaven by fitting himself with artificial wings and jumping out of a top-storey window — with the predictable result that he broke an arm. (According to some sources, this happened during the later stages of the scare rather than at the spring equinox itself, but the episode seems to be true.) The Millerites were not too depressed; 1843 still had many months to run, and it was too early to change course. Hines and his campaign managers continued the battle, and as the year drew to its end the hysteria was almost as great as ever. The panic had spread far and wide, and on 31 December a huge crowd gathered outside William Miller's house, no doubt anxious to receive the latest bulletins from on high. Still nothing happened. But Miller was not downhearted; suddenly he discovered a mistake in his predictions — they should have referred to the Jewish year, which was not due to end until 22 October 1844.

Clearly this was a serious blunder, but it could be put down to human fallibility, and the situation remained much as before. According to contemporary records, there were more than average numbers of admissions to lunatic asylums, and still the Millerites preached and thundered. Once more the crowds gathered. Once more, to their chagrin, the Lord refused to oblige. Miller made one more attempt; the end would come, he said, on the seventh day of the seventh month — but when this too passed without incident, he gave up. Joshua Hines retired from the arena (he lived to the age of ninety), and the Millerite movement faded away, with its members returning to their homes and doing their best to pick up the threads.

William Miller himself died soon afterwards. At least he had made his mark, and he never recanted; all that was wrong, he maintained, was the timescale. To him, the Book of Daniel was infallible. Probably he regretted that he had not been more accurate, but there was nothing that he could do about it – he did not even show any marked desire to saddle up a third white horse and accompany Lady Hester Stanhope to Jerusalem.

To the best of my knowledge, 'Second Coming', end-of-the-world predictions have been confined mainly to the United States. Miller's was by far the most notable, but there have been several since, one of which was sparked off in 1925 by two people: a Los Angeles girl, Margaret Rowan, and a German-born housepainter whose name was Robert Reidt. It was centred on California, and never spread further. Neither did it affect thousands of people, as the Millerite movement had done, but I feel that I ought to mention it. (I do not remember it myself, but as I was then at the early age of two, and lived in Bognor Regis, this is hardly surprising.) Reidt was based at Patchogue on Long Island, and his predictions were entirely Biblical. He gave the date of doom as 13 February, and so did Margaret Rowan – on the authority, she said, of no less a person than the Archangel Gabriel, who was presumably in an excellent position to know. The Messiah would appear in the eastern sky, in the form of a small cloud. He would draw closer, and on arrival would scorch the world to a crisp, wafting the faithful to Heaven while the sinners (that is to say, the bulk of the population) would be left to fend for themselves in the equivalent of Dante's Inferno.

Eyes were turned skywards on 6 February, when the Messiah was due to make his entry. However, the anticipated cloud failed to materialize, and by the 13th the Messiah was still an absentee. Both Margaret Rowan and Robert Reidt claimed that he had been detained for some reason or other, and would be along shortly, but the few hundred followers began to show signs of discontent, and gradually drifted away. What happened to the two prophets does not seem to be known, but at any rate nothing was heard from them.

Next came the Revd Charles G. Long, of Pasadena, who returned to the Book of Daniel. (This seems to be a favourite end-of-the-world text, though most people will remember it better for its description of a slight contretemps involving lions.) Long decided that the end would come at 5.33 pm, Pacific Time, on 21 September 1945. He founded a sect calling itself the Remnant of the Church of God, and for some years he preached away, gaining a few converts but failing to make much of an impact upon a world which was far more concerned with Adolf Hitler and the warlords of Japan. Seven days before the expected end, Long and his followers gave up eating (which was bearable) and drinking (which, under the circumstances, probably was not), and made their preparations. When 5.33 came and went, they gave resigned sighs and went back to their normal humdrum existence.

Next, in this admittedly very incomplete catalogue, I come to May 1954. This time the seat of activity was not America, but Rome, the Eternal City, where the Colosseum stands. According to legend, the world will come to an end when the Colosseum falls. When cracks suddenly started to appear in the fabric of the amphitheatre, people became alarmed. For some reason that I have been unable to discover, 24 May was regarded as D-day, and there was a noticeable panic in which many Romans endeavoured to allay their fears by means of alcohol. Not to put too fine a point on it, they became as drunk as newts. The Pope was not impressed, and went so far as to issue an official denial. This had a calming effect; the Colosseum still stands: the end of the world has not come yet.

Even during the last decade there have been at least two curious episodes. In 1992 a cult in South Korea announced that the end was imminent, and hundreds of people gathered in the expectation of being lifted heavenward in a cometlike flash known as 'the rapture'; when nothing happened they went home in disgust. In the same tradition, the Great White Brotherhood of the Ukraine predicted the end of the world for 24 November 1993 – later revised to 14 November because of a slight miscalculation. The main cult prophetess was a lady named Maria Khristos, who called herself Marina Tsvygun and announced that she was God. She managed to whip up a surprising degree of hysteria, and photographs of her, dressed in white robes and carrying a crucifix, were widely distributed. At the appointed time a large crowd assembled at the eleventh-century cathedral of St Sofia, in Kiev, which, proclaimed Marina, was 'the closest point to the cosmos'. Disturbances broke out when the police intervened, and fire extinguishers were used, covering much of the cathedral with foam. Eventually the crowd was dispersed, and Marina and her husband were taken into custody charged with various offences. Valentin Nedrehavlo, a spokesman for the Ukrainian Interior Ministry, closed the proceedings by declaring that 'Today is off. The end of the world is hereby cancelled.'

What are we to make of all this?

Without wishing to be irreligious, it is true to say that the Bible can be interpreted to mean almost anything provided that you are prepared to abandon all logic; it is merely a matter of taking passages out of context and stringing them together. (I remember a schoolboy essay in which it was shown, by means of perfectly correct quotes, that St Peter must have been a scratch golfer.) I do not think that any more 'Second Coming' stories of such a kind will gain much of a foothold today, and the biblical prophets of doom belong to the past. Of course, you never know, but it seems unlikely that anyone in AD 1999 dreamt of riding to Jerusalem on a white horse to meet the Creator. I would not consider trying it myself (even if I were capable of riding anything more ambitious than a bicycle), and I doubt whether anyone else will try it either.

The Astrologers

Not very long ago I had a letter from the secretary of a university students' union, inviting me to give a lecture. This, frankly, is nothing new; but I was intrigued by this one, because the writer asked whether I would be prepared to 'deliver a talk on the latest research in astrology'. What he meant was, of course, astronomy; it is incredible how 'in this day and age', to use one of those irritating 1999-type expressions, anyone can confuse the two. I was about to send a somewhat terse reply when I looked more carefully at the notepaper heading, and realised that the invitation came from a left-wing political group. This altered my attitude at once. Students of politics can hardly be expected to tell science from pseudo-science, and I rather unkindly referred the writer to the craziest astrologer I knew. I gather that the lecture was duly given, with interesting results!

I mention astrology here because it is very closely linked with end-of-the-world prophecies, and there have been several major panics, much the greatest being that of 1524, due directly to an eminent astrologer named Johann Stoffler. But before going any further, it is, I feel, essential to say something about astrology itself.

Basically, it is the superstition of the sky. Your character and destiny are supposed to depend upon the positions of the Sun, Moon and planets at the time of birth, so that, for instance, if you happen to have been born in London on 8 May you will be entirely different from a colleague who first saw the light of day on 7 September in Manchester. If I may be allowed to add a personal note: I made my entry on 4 March 1923, which means that my astrological sign is Pisces, the Fishes. I am therefore supposed to be gentle, kind, retiring, unlucky and often melancholy; I ought to spend much of my time at sea, or perhaps yachting or fishing; to care nothing for worldly power, and to be chronically unable to make money or even to keep what I have. Well – I suppose it is possible that I am gentle, kind and retiring, but when I suggested as much to a close friend he merely gave a bark of laughter and made some comments which I do not propose to reproduce here, if only because they would be of no interest to the reader. With regard to the sea, I admit to living within 500 yards of it, but I am no yachtsman; I paddle rather than swim, taking care to avoid treading upon sharp stones or slimy jellyfish; and I have never fished in my life, mainly because I would have a strong dislike of being yanked out of my natural habitat on the end of a bent pin, and I see no reason why any respectable fish should feel differently.

Astrologically, everything depends upon the positions of the planets against the starry background. There is a band stretching round the sky, known as the Zodiac, in which the Sun, Moon and principal planets are always to be found, because their paths are not sharply inclined to that of the Earth, and if you draw a plan of the Solar System upon a piece of flat paper you are not very far wrong. The Zodiac is divided into twelve constellations: Aries (the Ram), Taurus (the Bull), Gemini (the Twins), Cancer (the Crab), Leo (the Lion), Virgo (the Virgin), Libra (the Scales), Scorpio or Scorpius (the Scorpion),

Sagittarius (the Archer), Capricornus the (Sea-goat), Aquarius (the Water-bearer) and Pisces (the Fishes). Belonging as I do to Pisces, I come officially at the tail-end of the procession, though as a matter of fact that astrological signs are now out of step with the actual constellations, because the direction of the Earth's axis wobbles slightly, and this alters the positions of both the poles and the equator of the sky. From a purely astronomical point of view Pisces is now the first constellation of the Zodiac, not the last.

To explain this more fully, I must say a little about astronomical terms. The Earth spins on its axis once a day, and the direction of the axis indicates the position of the two celestial poles; the North Pole is marked fairly closely by the bright stat Polaris (there is no bright south polar star, the nearest naked-eye candidate being the obscure Sigma Octantis). And just as the terrestrial equator cuts the Earth in half, so the celestial equator cuts the sky in half, and we have a northern hemisphere and a southern hemisphere. As a matter of interest, the equator passes through the middle of the bright constellation of Orion, the Hunter.

Because the Earth completes one revolution round the Sun in one year (more accurately, in 365.25 days), the Sun itself seems to travel right round the sky in the same period. Its apparent path against the stars is known as the ecliptic, and because the Earth's axis is tilted to the perpendicular at an angle of 23½ degrees, the angle between the ecliptic and the celestial equator is also 23½ degrees. The points where the ecliptic and the equator cross are the equinoxes; the spring equinox or First Point of Aries when the Sun is travelling from south to north, and the Autumnal Equinox or First Point of Libra when the Sun is moving from north to south. In ancient times, the equinoxes really did lie in Aries and Libra respectively.

However, the Earth is not a perfect sphere. It bulges slightly at the equator (the equatorial diameter is twenty-six miles greater than the diameter as measured through the poles), and the Sun and Moon pull upon this bulge, causing the Earth to 'wobble' slightly in the manner of a gyroscope which is running down and has started to topple. The result is that the axis describes a small circle in the sky, over a period of about 26,000 years. Obviously this alters the positions of the celestial poles and hence, also, of the equinoxes. By now the First Point of Aries has shifted into the adjacent constellation, Pisces, while the First Point of Libra has moved into Virgo. This effect is known as precession, and explains why the astrological signs are now out of step with the constellations after which they are named – something which astrologers, as a class, prefer to forget.

Moreover, it is often forgotten that what we normally call a 'constellation' is not a true pattern at all. The stars are suns, and our Sun is nothing more than a run-of-the-mill star; modern astronomers even relegate it to the status of a stellar dwarf. It is, on average, 93 million miles away from us, but this is not much upon the astronomical scale, and all the other stars are far more remote, with distances which have to be measured in millions of millions of miles. For this reason, the mile is too short a unit of length to be convenient when we are discussing bodies beyond the Solar System, and a better unit is the light-year, which is a measure of length and not of time. Light moves at 186,000 miles per second, and yet it takes 4¼ years to reach us from the nearest star beyond the Sun; that is to say, this star (a dim red dwarf known as Proxima Centauri) is 4¼ light-years away. Sirius, the most brilliant star in the sky, is 8½ light-years away; Polaris lies at 680 light-years, and so on.

Now let us return to the constellations, and consider perhaps the most famous of them all – the Great Bear, known to astronomers as Ursa Major, to most Englishmen as the Plough, and to Americans as the Big Dipper. Its seven principal stars make up a pattern which cannot be misidentified, particularly since it is so far north in the sky that it never sets over the British Isles; you will always find it somewhere whenever the sky is sufficiently clear and dark. The two end stars in the Bear's tail are known as Mizar and Alkaid. (The names are Arabic; the official designations are Zeta and Eta Ursae Majoris respectively.) Mizar is fifty-nine light-years from us, while Alkaid is 108. Therefore the two stars are in no way associated, and merely happen to lie in much the same direction as seen from the Earth. In fact, Alkaid is much further away from Mizar than we are; and if we lay in the region between them, Mizar and Alkaid would be on opposite sides of the sky. (When you are measuring the distances of all but the nearest stars, there is bound to be some uncertainty. After all, we are dealing in distances of millions of millions of miles. In this book I am using the values given in the authoritative Cambridge Catalogue; other star catalogues give rather different values, but the principles involved are exactly the same.)

The same is true of other constellations, all of which are made up of entirely unassociated stars lying at very different distances. The patterns mean nothing at all, and in any case they are man-made. Nobody is quite sure who drew up the main constellation patterns which we now use; it may have been the Minoans of Ancient Crete, or the old Chaldaean shepherds who wanted to while away the long night hours. Extra groups have been added more recently; the sky contains such constellations as the Airpump, the Microscope and the Telescope, all of which would have looked rather out of place in classical times. (Other groups have been suggested. I particularly like Sceptrum Brandenburgicum, Officina Typographica and Honores Fredericii, but the International Astronomical Union put its foot firmly down fifty years ago, and reduced the accepted number of constellations to eighty-eight.)

Generally, the names of the constellations bear little resemblance to the forms of objects they are meant to represent. For example, anyone who can make a sea-goat out of the pattern of Capricornus earns my undying admiration. And, of course, other early civilizations had constellations of their own; the Egyptians included a hawk and a hippopotamus. We happen to follow the Greek system, suitably modified, but this was due merely to chance.

Come, then, to my own constellation of Pisces, the Fishes. It is very faint, and consists entirely of various dim stars spread out at random. Why it should be regarded as 'watery' is not clear, and why it should be associated with kindness, gentleness and financial incompetence makes even less sense. Neither do I see why the brighter but equally formless group of Taurus, the Bull, should be masculine and brash.

In a recent book* I even invented my own Zodiacal constellations, using real stars. For instance, I introduced a petrol-pump (*Antilia Gasolina*), a flying cow (*Vacca Volitans*), a duck-billed platypus (*Pendelanum Anorostrum Gravimerclae*) and the Abominable Snowman (*Homo Nivalis Vere, Vere Horribilis*). They are just as valid as those used by today's astrologers!

Next, what of the planets? There are eight of them, all moving round the Sun at different distances: Mercury, Venus, the Earth, Mars, Jupiter, Saturn, Uranus and Neptune. The last two were not known in ancient times, and were discovered in 1781 and 1846 respectively, though they seem to have had little difficulty in fitting into the general astrological theme. But there are extra problems here! Pluto, discovered in 1930, was regarded as a proper planet, and astrologers used it in all their horoscopes. However, it gradually became evident that Pluto was was not a proper planet at all. It is smaller than our own moon, smaller than some of the satellites of the giant planets, and

* *Stars of Destiny*, Canopus, 2006

not the only body of that kind moving in the far reaches of the Solar System. In fact, there is a whole swarm of them, and one member, Eris, is larger than Pluto, while others are comparable. So if you regard Pluto as a planet, as the astrologers did, you have to include dozens of others and things become hopelessly complicated. Up to now the astrologers do not seem to have had the answer, and they have to admit they are totally baffled.

In astrology, a planet is said to be 'in' a constellation when it is seen against the background of stars making up that particular constellation. Thus in July 2009 Mars was 'in' Taurus. Yet Mars is close on the cosmical scale. It may come within 35 million miles of us, which is negligible. To say that Mars is 'in' Virgo is about as logical as holding up your finger against a cloudy sky and claiming that your finger is 'in' the clouds.

These, then, are the facts. The positions of the Sun, Moon and planets at the time of birth are all-important astrologically, and so are their subsequent movements; thus if Saturn and Mars seem close together it may mean that disaster lies ahead, so that there is no chance whatsoever of a happy meeting with a dark lady coming over the water. A year or two ago I cast my horoscope, and found that according to all the omens I ought to have a major success at some physical activity. I was playing cricket that day, and so far as I can remember my bowling analysis was 0 for 87. Clearly there had been a slight error somewhere or other.

In short: the planets are essentially local, the stars are very remote indeed, and the constellation patterns have no real significance. Neither, therefore, have the astrological signs, which are in any case out of step. It is also true that an extra constellation (Ophiuchus, the Serpent-bearer) intrudes into the Zodiac between Scorpius and Sagittarius, but has not been given a sign of its own, because all the vacant places have been taken and the hapless Serpent-bearer has been left out on a limb.

Curiously, Ophiuchus was again in the news quite recently, when a misleading television broadcast by a well-known astronomer managed to give the impression that a new Zodiacal sign had been discovered. Astrologers were thrown into disarray. Would they have to revise all their horoscopes in order to cater for the newcomer? They were immensely relieved to find that the intrusion of Ophiuchus into the Zodiac had been common knowledge for over two thousand years. They were able to relax; the crisis was over.

Astrology goes back a long way, to the time when the Earth was regarded as the most important of all bodies, and believed to lie in the centre of the universe. Most astronomers of olden days were also astrologers, and up to the time of Isaac Newton – that is to say, the late seventeenth century – astrology was still regarded as a true science. Ancient rulers and generals placed great faith in astrologers, and at least one major war was swung upon astrological advice. This was the Peloponnesian War, fought between the Greek city-states of Athens and Sparta. I do not want to delve into history, but it is worth recording that when the Athenians had invaded the island of Sicily, and were in danger of annihilation, their commander, Nicias, delayed evacuation because of an eclipse of the Moon, which, said the astrologers, meant that he had better stay where he was. He did; and he never had another chance to escape. That, in the long run, was the end of Athens as a great power.

Astrology still lingers on in two guises: that of the 'What the Stars Foretell' newspaper columnists, and the serious practitioners, who are in deadly earnest, casting horoscopes and handing themselves impressive degrees such as DF Astrol.S. It is common in India, and it was widely reported that one Prime Minister, Mrs Indira Ghandi, timed the 1971 election on astrological advice – I admit, winning it handsomely – while in January 1982 the date of the marriage of Princess Chulabhorn, daughter of King Bhumibol of Thailand, was fixed at a moment which the Court astrologers regarded as propitious. Indeed, in Thailand, a general election in 1991 was actually affected by astrological advice.

The reigning coalition government had been defeated, and the incoming Prime Minister was General Chatichai Coonhavan, who was nothing if not astrologically-minded. His consultant told him that all names for his new coalition would have to be announced on the Friday following the election. Naturally, the General obeyed. Unfortunately the Social Action party, which had been the second largest of the outgoing coalition, had arranged to announce its nominees on the Saturday, by which time it was too late. Mr Kukrit Pramoj, leader of the excluded party, was justifiably annoyed. 'When we asked why all the hurry,' he said, 'they told us that they had to stick to the astrologer's advice. Before we could do anything, the new Cabinet was appointed without us in it.'

Astrology has had many famous supporters, such as the eccentric educationalist Rudolf Steiner (who also believed the Earth to be flat) and even Hitler, who apparently believed the astrologers who told him that the Western Powers would not dare to go to war in 1939. Not surprisingly, psychiatrists and psychologists tend to be sympathetic. C.G. Jung was one devotee. There has recently been qualified support from a professional astronomer, Dr P.A.H. Seymour and also from the late H.J. Eysenck and his colleague D.K.B. Nias, who published a book in which they gave some credence to a French husband-and-wife team, the Gauquelins, about whom it is worth saying a little more.

Basically, the Gauquelins have been tabulating the positions of the planets at the times of birth and death of people in certain definite walks of life. Since the Earth is spinning round, each planet appears to rise and set once every twenty-four hours (though, of course, this often happens in daylight). The planets rise in an easterly direction, reach their highest point at the moment of culmination – termed by the astrologers 'midheaven' – and set towards the west. The Gauquelins divided the apparent path of each planet across the sky into twelve sectors, and concluded that the risings and settings of the planets were of real significance. Thus, if a baby happened to be born when Mars or Saturn was rising, he (or she) was quite likely to become a doctor. Mars was linked with sportsmen – and after all, Mars himself was the virile God of War …

Of course, things were not quite right. In particular, the Sun and Moon seemed to have no effect at all. Neither did Mercury, or the two outer planets Uranus and Neptune. Of all the Solar System bodies studied by most astrologers, the Gauquelins therefore promptly threw out six, because they did not fit in. It then became painfully clear that with ordinary people even the effects of the four remaining bodies (Venus, Mars, Jupiter and Saturn) did not fit either. The choice of personalities had to be narrowed down, and at length, after casting aside more than half the bodies of the Solar System and selecting suitable groups of people, they decided that they had reached some results which were really significant.

Let it be said at once that there is no doubt about the sincerity of the Gauquelins, or those psychiatrists who have investigated their findings. Thousands of tests have been carried out. But it is hard to see how the results can be taken seriously, because if you juggle with figures for long enough it would indeed be odd if no apparent relationships could be found. Given enough patience, it is possible to prove practically anything. Not long ago I was giving a lecture in London to an audience composed of people from all walks of life, and I decided to carry out an astrological test of my own. The audience nobly filled in the questionnaires that I distributed. Upon analysing the results, I found that a significant percentage of those born under the sign of Leo disliked beetroot, while Aquarius appeared to be linked with tennis players, and male members of the audience who had been born under Aries tended to have Christian names beginning with the letters C, R or T.

Before leaving the Gauquelins, I wonder what they would conclude from the horoscope of a baby born in North Norway during the spring of 1982, when all four planets were so far south of the celestial equator that as seen from that part of the world they never rose at all? Presumably the luckless infant would be deprived of all the advantages of astrological influences!

You cannot but admire the astrologers' techniques. Most of their predictions are so tightly wrapped in cotton wool that they can be interpreted in almost any way, and when asked just why the positions of the planets can affect human destiny they admit, with refreshing candour, that they don't know. It has something to do with Vibrations, but that is as much as they can say.

I have often been asked to give my views about astrology, and I always given the same answer. It proves one scientific fact – 'There's one born every minute!'

I apologise for this somewhat lengthy digression, but I felt it necessary because throughout the ages the astrologers have been vocal in predicting that the end is nigh. What alarmed them most (and still does) is a gathering of planets in any one particular part of the heavens. Of course, we are again dealing with line-of-sight effects; if, for instance, Venus and Jupiter happen to lie side by side, we must not jump to the conclusion that they are genuinely close together. On average, Venus is 67 million miles from the Sun, while for Jupiter the distance is 483 million miles, so that the two planets must always be hundreds of millions of miles apart. Appearances can be deceptive.

The planets move round the sun not only at different distances, but also in widely differing periods, ranging from eighty-eight days in the case of Mercury up to almost 165 years for Pluto. Inevitably, then, there are times when they enter the same part of the Zodiac. There was a major conjunction of several planets in the year 1186, and this was quite enough for the astrologers to forecast all sorts of dire events, which, however, failed to materialise. Yet the climax was reached in 1524, and now we come, at last, to Johan Stoffler.

Stoffler was born in Lustingen, in Suebia, in 1452. He was certainly no dunce, and he made his way to the University of Tubingen, where he soon became well known. He wrote various books, mainly on astrology, as well as an excellent treatise on the ancient astronomical measuring instrument known as the astrolabe; he was also concerned with calendar reform. His fame spread, and he was regarded as a very wise man indeed. One story about him (possibly apocryphal, though I would like to believe it!) relates how the stars told him that on a certain day he would be in grave danger from a falling body. Prudently he stayed indoors, but made the elementary mistake of reaching for a book which lay on a high shelf; the book made an unceremonious descent, and landed upon his head, which did not please him in the least even though he had proved his point.

During his routine calculations, Stoffler suddenly made a dramatic discovery. In February 1524 the planets Mars, Jupiter and Saturn would all be in Pisces. Of course, Pisces is a watery sign; Mars and Saturn are generally of evil influence –and the only logical result would be a great flood, which would destroy itself. Nothing could be more straightforward.

Stoffler felt it his duty to issue a general warning, and accordingly he did so. Other astrologers agreed with him and, as 1524, approached there was evidence of panic. Almanacs sprang up like mushrooms, all bearing the same message, and the alarm was not confined to Germany.

It spread over much of Europe – not, so far as I can tell, to England – and even penetrated to parts of Asia and Africa; Stoffler's reputation was so great that nobody felt inclined to doubt him. According to contemporary reports, the terror far surpassed that inspired by the Millerites long afterwards. Moreover, many Top People joined in.

What was to be done? If water were to be the main agent of destruction, the obvious remedy was to build boats, and this is precisely what many people did. In France, President Auriol of the University of Toulouse set to work building what was to all intents and purposes a Noah-type ark. Not that he meant to collect any animals; he wanted the ark for himself and his nearest and dearest, but an ark it was, none the less. All over Europe, trade and commerce came to a grinding halt. The essential thing was to build boats, boats and still more boats, so that before long the Rhine was more crowded than the Serpentine on a sunny summer's day. Fields were left uncultivated, and most of the ordinary routine of life was in abeyance. Some people decided to drink themselves to death rather than face the coming holocaust, while others adopted pious attitudes and resolved to make the best of it. There were cases of men and women who sold all their possessions in order to finance their boat-building, while others made haste to the tops of mountains, presumably hoping that the peaks would poke out above the raging waters.

Royalty was not unaffected. The Emperor Charles V of Spain sent out his wise men to look for safe places, assuming that the floods would not be total and that some parts of the world would escape being drowned – if, of course, the world survived at all. Another story, perhaps again apocryphal, relates how a German count named von Iggleheim was attacked by a fear-crazed mob when he refused to share his boat with the common people, and was fatally injured. As 20 February approached, the day given by Stoffler, the panic reached its height. Nothing like it had been seen in Europe before, and probably nothing like it will be seen again.

Ironically, most of February was dry and warm, but on the 21st rain began and continued steadily until everything was wet and soggy. Still, this was very different from a major flood, and as March began the general panic started to abate. Could there have been an error? One man who thought so was Johann Carion, astrologer to the Emperor Joachim I of Brandenburg. Stoffler, said Carion, was wrong. The date of the disaster was not 20 February, but 15 July of the following year, 1525. By then things had more or less reverted to normal over most of the mainland, but the Elector prudently decided that he had better take action.

Once again I depend upon contemporary reports which may or may not be reliable. If they are, then the afternoon of 15 July witnessed a strange scene. As the clouds gathered, the gates of the Castle of Berlin-Koln were flung open, and the State coach came out, carrying the Elector and his family; behind it were other vehicles, containing all the most treasured family possessions which were even remotely portable. The procession made its way to the top of a nearby hill, where it stayed until nightfall. The only celestial manifestation was a shower, and eventually the Elector decided to go home, leaving Carion behind in disgrace. Just as the coach arrived back at the castle gates, a flash of lightning struck it and killed all four horses. The Elector immediately recalled Carion, though what happened later is not on record.

Slowly the last traces of panic died away, but there were echoes of it for some time. President Auriol dismantled his ark, and when questioned about it said rather lamely that he had merely wanted it for a fishing trip. Stoffler himself was not in the least abashed, and produced another prediction, this time for 1588: 'If in this terrible year the globe is not dissolved to dust, and the land and sea be not destroyed, every kingdom will be overthrown and humanity will suffer pain.' By that time Stoffler would have reached the ripe old age of 148, so presumably he felt justified in taking a chance. He actually died in 1531, and nothing happened in 1588 apart, of course, from the Spanish Armada which had no astrological connections whatever. Note, however, that this time Stoffler was not relying upon any planetary conjunction. He selected that particular date because it was the eighth year following the 1,580th anniversary of the birth of Christ.

Another astrologer, one Cyprian Leowitz, drew attention to a conjunction due in 1584 – not so imposing as Stoffler's, but still marked enough to be alarming. According to a contemporary writer named Louis Guyon, 'the terror of the populace was extreme, and the churches could not hold the multitudes which fled to them for refuge; many made their wills without stopping to think that this would avail them little if the world were really to perish, while others donated goods to the clergy, in the hope that their prayers would postpone the Day of Judgement'.

Before passing on, let us pause to dispose of two characters who were not specifically concerned with astrology, but who nevertheless claimed to be able to see into the future. One was Mother Shipton, who is believed to have lived from 1488 to 1562, in which case she was Stoffler's contemporary. There is little doubt that Mother Shipton really existed, though she is so deeply woven into legend that it is impossible to separate truth from myth, and she seems to have been the prototype of those withces so roughly treated by Sir Rupert Murgatroyd in Ruddigore. ('Sir Rupert Murgatroyd, his leisure and his riches/He ruthlessly employed in persecuting witches.') Apparently, she predicted the Fire of London, and one verse attributed to her reads:

Houses shall appear in the vales below,
And covered by hail and snow;
The world then to an end shall come
In nineteen hundred and ninety-one.

The other seer was Nostradamus, whose fame is still great
even today. He was French, and lived from 1503 to 1566.
He specialised in rhyming prophecies, and several times he
hit the nail squarely on the head. (Coincidence? Probably.
As was once said, 'it is impossible always to be wrong',
unless of course you happen to be a psychiatrist.) Among
Nostradamus' Centuries we find:

Quand Georges Dieu crucifiera
Que Marc le ressuscitera,
Et que St Jean le portera,
La fin du monde arrivera.

To translate: when Easter falls on 25 April (St Mark's Day),
Holy Friday will be on 23 April (St George's Day) and
Corpus Christi on 24 June (St John's Day), and the world
will end. It was Camille Flammarion, the celebrated French
astronomer, who pointed out that there is something odd
about this. The calendar was not reformed until 1582, when
it was officially changed from the old Julian into the modern
Gregorian. Before that, Easter could not possibly fall on 25
April, and yet Nostradamus died in 1566. Since then, Easter
has fallen on 25 April (its last possible date) in 1666, 1734,
1886 and 1943. The next occasion will be in 2038. Let us
hope that Nostradamus was wrong.

Another verse (Century One, section or quatrain 48)
gives a rather different story:

Vingt ans regne de la lune passez,
Sept mil ans autre tiendra sa monarche'

Quand le Soleil prendra ses jours lasses,
Lors accomplit et mine ma prophetie,

or, 'When twenty years of the Moon's reign have passed, another will take up his reign for 7,000 years. When the exhausted Sun takes up his cycle, then my prophecy and my threats will be accomplished.' If Nostradamus believed that he was writing at the start of a new 'cycle of the Moon', there is a link with an old Middle Ages theory that the world will come to an end at the beginning of the seventh millennium, an idea coming originally from the Book of Enoch, which was removed by the Church from the Canon in AD 300. Nostradamus also has a relevant passage in Century Ten, quatrain 74, the translation of which is: 'The year of the great seventh number accomplished, it will appear at the time of the games of slaughter, not far from the age of the great millennium when the dead will come out of their graves.'

Candidly I am not particularly impressed with Nostradamus, who was at best obscure, and will do no more than mention the eclipse of 12 August 1654, interpreted as being decidedly menacing, though for no obvious reason. When the world failed to end, one clergyman preached a sermon in which he said that God had relented, and had given humanity a fortnight's grace, so that he had postponed not only the Last Trump but also the eclipse itself. So let us skip several hundred years and come to our own age, with Professor Porta's 'League of Planets' and, in particular, Dr John Gribbin's 'Jupiter Effect'.

The Jupiter Effect

Astrologers depend for their forecasts on the positions of the planets against the starry background. Their end-of-the-world predictions have been based upon mysticism and occultism, to say nothing of those elusive 'vibrations'. However, there have been other scares connected with the planets, not for their astrological powers, but for their purely physical effects. And first in the field seems to have been Professor Alberto Porta.

Porta was an oddity. I have never been able to find out whether he was really entitled to be called a professor; I have a nasty suspicion that he wasn't, though I may be doing him an injustice. He was Italian-born, but emigrated to the United States at some time during the 1870s, and studied seismology and meteorology. He did have some success in predicting earthquakes, though again it was probably sheer luck (even today we cannot tell just when or where earthquakes will strike, though we know a great deal more about them than we did a few decades ago). Porta published weather forecasts in San Francisco, where there was a small newspaper printed in Italian for the benefit of immigrants, and in 1917 he gave his opinion that there would be a violent shock along the

Pacific coast on either 27 or 28 December. On the 25th, a serious tremor ruined Guatemala City, and further jolts occurred on the following days, so that Porta's warnings came to be taken quite seriously by the general public.

He then turned his attention to the planets and found, quite correctly, that in December 1919 most of them would be roughly lined up. Mercury, Venus, Mars, Jupiter, Saturn and Neptune were on one side of the Sun, and Uranus on the other side, so that all of them were pulling gravitationally in the same sense. Porta called it the 'League of Planets', and drew dire conclusions from it.

According to his theory, sunspots, the dark patches on the solar disc, were produced by the electromagnetic pulls of the planets. Actually, we now know – or think we know – that the planets have nothing to do with sunspots; there is a semi-regular cycle of eleven years, when sunspots are particularly numerous, so that the Sun was very active in 1958, 1969, 1980 and 2000, and should be again in 2011. The spots are centres of strong magnetic fields, and violent outbursts known as flares, associated with them, emit streams of charged particles which enter our upper atmosphere and interfere with wireless reception, as well as producing aurorae or polar lights and causing the compass needle to fluctuate. However, the origin of all these phenomena lies in the Sun itself, not outside. Porta's ideas were very different. I quote:

Owing to the strange grouping of six mighty planets such as has not been seen for a score of centuries, the United States will next December be swept by the most terrific weather cataclysm since human history began. It will be caused by the largest sunspot on record. It will appear on 17 December 1919, as a vast wound in the side of the Sun – a gigantic explosion of flaming gases, leaping hundreds of thousands of miles out into space. It will be rich enough in electromagnetic waves to fling the atmosphere of our planet into a disturbance without precedent or parallel. There will be hurricanes, lightning, colossal rains. There will also be gigantic lava eruptions, great earthquakes, to say nothing of floods and fearful cold . . . Six planets will be massed in the narrow limit of 26 degrees on the same side of the Sun. Directly opposite, coming into opposition with this gigantic League of Planets, will be the huge planet Uranus. The magnetic currents between Uranus and the six planets will pierce the Sun like a mighty spear. Be warned in advance. Tremendous events will happen from 17 to 20 December 1919, and afterwards!

In view of his previous successes, Porta's words caused some panic, though it could not be compared even remotely with those caused by Stoffler or Miller. The Nautical Almanac Office of the United States Naval Observatory was bombarded by anxious enquirers, and was forced to issue a disclaimer, but people kept a wary eye on the Sun, and it is related that some miners in Oklahoma refused to go underground in case they would be trapped. (This is surely an original reason for a strike!) In fact no exceptional sunspots appeared, and there were no earthquakes. I may add that the largest sunspot on record, that of April 1947, did not coincide with any planetary conjunctions.

I may be accused of cheating here, because up to now I have been discussing the actual end of the world, and this was not what Porta predicted; all he said was that his 'League of Planets' would produce serious disturbances, which is not the same thing. After the usual and inevitable anti-climax, he went back to forecasting gales and minor earthquakes. I have been unable to find out what eventually happened to him. He had had his moment of notoriety, and he subsided gently into the background.

An interesting planetary conjunction in 1962 passed off without much comment, though astrologers in India were somewhat alarmed by it. So we come now to the work of two British science writers, John Gribbin, then of Sussex University, and his colleague Stephen Plagemann. Let it be said at once that they come into a different category from Alberto Porta. First, they have perfectly valid degrees in astronomy; secondly, their forecasts depend upon gravitational forces rather than electromagnetic ones. Yet in a way they have come back to what may be termed a 'League of Planets', and their book, *The Jupiter Effect*, first published in 1974 and since released several times, created a tremendous amount of interest, mixed with alarm.

The main theme of the book was that during 1982 all the main planets would line up, in a 'superconjunction' which would cause dire effects upon the Earth. Jupiter, the most massive of the planets, would have the main triggering effect – hence the title of the book. But before going on, it seems only right to say something about the overall pattern of the Solar System itself.

Of course the controlling body is our own star, the Sun, which is a huge globe approximately 865,000 miles in diameter and with a mass almost 330,000 times that of the Earth. (You could pack a million bodies the volume of the Earth inside the Sun and still leave plenty of room to spare.) The surface temperature is almost 6,000°C, and the temperature at the core reaches the incredible value of at least 15,000,000°C. It is radiating not because it is burning, but because of nuclear reactions taking place inside it, a point to which I will return later. Even mighty Jupiter has less than one-thousanth the mass of the Sun.

The Solar System is divided neatly into two parts. The inner region contains four comparatively small, solid planets: Mercury, Venus, the Earth and Mars, with mean distances from the Sun ranging from 36 million miles for Mercury out to 141.5 million miles for Mars. Beyond Mars there is a wide gap, in which move thousands of worlds known as the asteroids or minor planets. Beyond this again come the giants: Jupiter, Saturn, Uranus and Neptune, all of which are much larger than the Earth and are of completely different make-up, with solid cores, mainly liquid interiors and outer layers of gas. Finally there is the strange little world Pluto, which seems to be in a class of its own and may not be worthy of true planetary status.

Because the revolution periods are so different, it is only natural that there must be times when the planets move into an approximate line. In their original book, Gribbin and Plagemann stated that between 1977 and 1982 the planets of the Solar System would move into an unusual alignment in which every planet would be in conjunction with every other planet, so that all the planets would be aligned on the same side of the Sun. Such an alignment occurs only once in 179 years. They went on to predict a depressing sequence of events:

1 The combined gravitational pulls of the planets would stretch out the Sun.

2 This tidal stretching would cause great disturbances on the solar surface, increasing the numbers of sunspots and solar activity in general.

3 The active areas of the Sun would shoot out electrified particles, many of which would shower on to the Earth.

4 Consequently, the Earth's rate of rotation would be altered, either by the effects of the charged particles on our own magnetic field, or by interactions with the Earth's atmosphere, thereby altering the overall atmospheric circulation and increasing the friction between the air and the solid ground.

5 This change in rotation, even though very small, would cause strains in the Earth's globe, triggering off earthquakes along lines of weakness in the crust.

In particular they mentioned the San Francisco area, where a weak line in the Earth's crust known as the San Andreas Fault has long been viewed with misgivings. There was a major quake in 1906, which devastated the city, and there will almost certainly be another in the foreseeable future.

All this sounds plausible enough, but there are two immediate objections. One is that no planetary alignment was due between 1977 and 1982, as any rough calculation would show. In 1982, the Gribbin 'critical year', it was quite true that the planets were in the same quadrant of the Solar System, but there was not even an approximate lining-up. Look, for instance, at the situation in March 1982. The angular distance between two of the giants, Saturn and Neptune, was not far short of a right angle!

The second fatal objection could be demonstrated by simple subtraction. According to Gribbin and Plagemann, the 'alignment' occurs every 179 years. Take 179 away from 1982; we have 1803, and there was no major earthquake anywhere near that date; we have to go back to 1783 (in the Calabria area of Italy) or forwards to 1811 (a series of shocks in New Madrid, in the United States).

It has been calculated that the tidal stretching of the Sun could never amount to more than a few millimetres at most, which is not much when considering a globe 865,000 miles in diameter. Moreover, we now know that the solar surface pulsates up and down to the extent of about six miles in periods ranging from several minutes to several hours, which is more than enough to mask any planetary effects completely. (Remember, the Sun contains 99.86 per cent of the entire mass of the Solar System.) Another way of putting it is that the maximum planetary tides on the Sun are about 2,700,000 times smaller than the Moon's tidal effects upon the Earth.

It is also interesting to work out the tidal pulls on the Sun caused by each planet, taking the Earth's pull as unity. The figures are as follows:

Mercury (maximum)	1.89
Venus	0.54
Earth	1
Mars (maximum)	0.041
Jupiter	2.26
Saturn	0.11
Uranus	0.002
Neptune	0.0006

Therefore we can promptly forget all about Mars and the four outer planets, which even when combined have negligible pulls compared with that of Jupiter. The idea that they could produce any measurable effects is not valid. Gribbin also forecast that the 'alignment' would delay the time of sunspot maximum until 1982. It didn't.

Nevertheless, a scare had been started, and a programme at the London Planetarium entitled 'Omens' did not help the situation in the least, because it treated the theory seriously. I did persuade the Planetarium officials to take it off, but not before I had begun to receive letters from parents whose children had been badly frightened, and as 1982 approached many official bodies – including the Kitt Peak National Observatory in America, and the Royal Greenwich Observatory in England – were forced to issue denials. Even in my own case I must have received at least 500 letters about it, and though I presented a special *Sky at Night* programme on BBC television the letters continued to pour in.

By now the scare had spread beyond Europe and the United States. There were minor panics in India, where people turned to astrologers for advice; a guru called B.V. Raman rassured them by saying that only Los Angeles would be destroyed, not the whole world. On the critical day, 10 March, the New Delhi *Herald* forecast that the planetary alignment would cause disease, riots, labour unrest and, of course, an earthquake, while 'a strange epidemic affecting the abdomen' would stalk India. The Brahmin priests in Calcutta performed special ceremonies, which involved the kindling of small fires and paying tribute to the fire-god Agni. Over in Peking (or, to give it its modern name, Beijing) the *Youth Daily* reissued a statement from the Chinese Government to the effect that any fears about the approaching end of the world were groundless.

Things were no better in the United States. One astronomer at Kitt Peak received an agitated call from an elderly woman; her grandson had his ninth birthday on 10 March – would he survive to see it? On the day itself came a programme transmitted from many local radio stations featuring one Boyd Quate, a long-range weather forecaster. The programme had been compiled by the News Information Weekly Service (NIWS) and was compered by Harold Joffe from Portsmouth, Virginia.

Following a general introduction, Joffe stated that sunspots and magnetic outbreaks on the solar surface 'have everything to do with our weather, and they are under the influence of the "Jupiter Effect"'. After a contribution from Quate, to the effect that something in outer space was disturbing his magnetic data (whatever they might have been), Joffe turned to the exceptionally cold winter over North America, which again he attributed to the unusual planetary alignment. He went on: 'Scientific correlations between the "Jupiter Effect" and the weather are sketchy, but they occur none the less', and Quate agreed that 'it does happen'. Perhaps fittingly, the programme ended with a contribution from an astrologer, Carole Davine, who was quite sure that 'there is no area of living which is not being affected' by the alignment, and that 'the US chart will be under a lot of stress this year. If there is going to be a war, it would be inclined to start during this time.'

All in all it was a remarkable episode, and it demonstrates that even in the Space Age any wild rumour is liable to spread once it has been sparked off.

(In a further article, Dr Gribbin has described planetary alignments and ancient Chinese ideas about them which indicate that there may be effects on our climate, with even a new Ice Age on the way. Fortunately I don't think this will happen either. There is no conceivable reason why it should!)

Now for another curiosity. In August 1987 Dr Jose Argueilles, an art historian, found that all the planets would line up in a way which had not happened for 23,412 years (please do not ask me how he arrived at this figure). Using astrology, Mayan and Aztec lore, he concluded that it was essential for 144,000 people to 'resonate together' – that is to say, hum – in order to avert cosmic disasters which would include a galactic beam as well as a deluge of flying saucers. People listened, and thousands of Americans went to the tops of mountains and hummed. The flying saucers stayed away, the galactic beam was not in evidence, and the world is still here, so that presumably the manoeuvre was successful. I assure you that this story is actually true!

Glossing over a routine doomsday prediction made for February 1993, when French astrologers predicted a planetary alignment similar to that which had taken place on the day of the death of Napoleon, we come at last to 5 May 2000. The prophets are already at work, and I can do no better than quote a headline in the London *Daily*

Express for 5 May 1998. It reads: *COUNTDOWN TO THE DOOMSDAY LINE-UP. Insurance warned of worst disaster since the days of the Pharaohs.* To continue:

> It looks like an astrologer's dream come true. The day when the Earth, Sun, Moon and five other planets come into line for the first time since the Pharaohs ruled Egypt. It will happen two years from today, on 5 May 2000. However, it will not be an event which will pass off quietly. Stand by for tidal waves, earthquakes and volcanic eruptions. In other words – Doomsday, says a leading risk expert, Dr Julian Salt.
>
> The normally cautious insurance industry is taking the threat so seriously that Dr Salt has been hired to advise top London underwriting agency D.P. Mann. Yesterday he urged Government to prepare for a day that could spell doom for millions. He went on to predict tidal waves up to a mile high, and that the exceptional 'pull from space' could release the boiling heat and energy of the Earth's core by ruptures of the outer crust. A spate of volcanoes could in turn bring ruin and starvation in its wake by changing the Earth's climate.

Actually, the planets were spread out over 30 degrees of the sky. This is very different from the conjunction of, say, February 1861, when the main planets were within a few degrees of each other. Even the 1982 conjunction was more compact than that of 2000, so that insurance companies had no cause for alarm. My efforts to contact Dr Julian Salt were signally unsuccessful. I wonder what he said when he woke up on the morning of 6 May 2000?

Yet though the effects on Earth are nil, the arrangement of the major planets in a gentle curve near the end of the 1970s proved to be a boon to the spacecraft planners. Mars, Venus and Mercury can be reached in a few months, but the outer members of the Sun's family are much further away. Jupiter is reasonably accessible, in less than two years, but then there is a vast gap before we reach the orbit of Saturn, and Uranus and Neptune are more remote still. You tend to forget how spread out the giant planets really are, and an ordinary map of the Solar System can be misleading, just as an average European may look at a chart of the southern hemisphere and think that it is almost possible to stand on the Queensland coast of Australia and hop across to New Zealand. If a spacecraft is destined to go to Uranus, for instance, then the orbit of Saturn is less than half-way.

The favoured method is to use the technique which I have rather irreverently called interplanetary snooker. It involves using the gravitational pull of one planet to send the spacecraft hurtling out towards another. Thus Voyager 2, launched in 1977, by-passed Jupiter in 1979; it was swung round the giant planet towards a rendezvous with Saturn, which was duly accomplished in 1981.

Saturn's pull was then used to send Voyager out to Uranus, which was encountered in January 1986, after which Uranus was used to dispatch the probe out to an encounter with Neptune in August 1989. Voyager 2 will never return; it is on its way out of the Solar System, and in millions of years from now it may still be wandering unheard between the stars. Without this 'gravity assist' technique it would have taken much longer to reach Uranus and Neptune, and it is quite true that this lining-up will not recur for the best part of two centuries.

Finally, mention must be made of Monsieur Louis Jacot, whose theories were published in 1977 in a book entitled *Earth's Flight Beyond* (beyond what, I am frankly unsure). Monsieur Jacot believes that space is filled with a substance called ether, and that the Sun throws out planets now and then, after which these planets move outwards in spiral paths. There is a kind of general post, with Mercury moving out to the orbit of Venus, Venus to that of the Earth, and so on. As the distances increase, the density of the surrounding ether falls away; the planets expand, and eventually go off 'pop'. This he takes to be the ultimate fate of the Earth, though not, I am glad to say, for a long time yet.

Monsieur Jacot's warnings, given in deep sincerity, have not really impressed the scientific world. In fact it may be said that they have caused all the impact of a feather falling on to damp blotting-paper, and they are not likely to cause anything in the way of alarm. But they are intriguing none the less, and I, for one, read them with marked, albeit rather stunned, fascination.

I am afraid that this has been a rather discursive chapter, but it has had to cover quite a number of ideas, some of them less logical than others. Astrology, that weird relic of the past, hangs on grimly, but we can certainly discount Professor Porta's electromagnetic forces as agents of destruction, and neither need we have any fear of planetary alignments.

What, then, of the planets themselves? I need only say that they move in completely stable paths, and the notion that any of them will 'run wild' and crash into us will make any mathematician smile pityingly. I will return to this theme later, when discussing Dr Velikovsky, but I can assure you that there is no need for any misgivings. Yet it was Saturn which produced a curious if minor scare in the little town of Dinkelsbühl, forty miles from Nürnberg, as recently as 1946. For some reason which I have been utterly unable to discover, the rumour went round that Saturn had fallen out of its orbit, and was racing towards us in the manner of a homing pigeon. The Allied authorities, at that time firmly in charge of Germany, found that there was marked reluctance on the part of the local inhabitants to leave their homes in order to go to work, and efforts were made to track down the source of the rumour. I do not think that it was ever unravelled, and before long the fears died away. Presumably muttering things such as 'Donner und Blitzen!' 'Damit!' and 'Besonders', everyone went back to work. Saturn is still intact. So is Dinkelsbühl. And so are we.

The Menacing Moon

O Moon, lovely Moon with the beautiful face,
Careering throughout the bound'ries of space,
Whenever I see you, I think in my mind
Shall I ever, O ever, behold thy behind?

I first came across this rhyme many years ago, when, at the
age of about nine, I started to take more than a passing
interest in the Moon. From all accounts it was written by
a housemaid in the service of a well-known poet, who had
done her best to combine verse with sheer science. Actually
there was more than a grain of truth in the rhyme, because
the Moon does keep the same face turned permanently
towards us, and from the Earth there is 41 per cent of the
lunar surface which we can never see. Until 1959, when the
Russians despatched their camera-carrying vehicle, Luna 3,
on a round trip and managed to obtain photographs of the
hidden regions, the 'other side of the Moon' was completely
unknown. Today, of course, there are 27 men who have seen
it – the crews of Apollos 8 and 10 to 17 inclusive – and we
know that it is just as barren and just as crater-crusted as the
hemisphere we can see on any clear night when the Moon
is well placed.

Why does the Moon behave in this curious way? The answer may be summed up in two words: 'tidal friction', and it is this tidal friction which has led some people to suggest that the Moon will eventually destroy the Earth, or at least all life on it. As I am particularly fond of the Moon, I must say at the outset that this will not happen; but before going into any more detail, let me discuss another theory which once had a considerable following, and which was linked, in a way, with the end of the world.

It originated with an Austrian engineer named Hans Hörbiger. I never met him (he died before the Second World War), but I have known people who did, and it is generally agreed that he was an odd character by any standards. His classic book, *Glazial Kosmogonie*, was published in 1913. I have not read it, because (rather naturally) it is written in German, and my knowledge of the Teutonic language was – and still is – limited to 'Damit', 'Besonders' and 'Donner und Blitzen'. Since it has never been fully translated, I have not read the complete version even now; it runs to almost 800 pages, and is crammed with diagrams, photographs and portmanteau words. From all accounts of it, plus the sections which have been rendered into English, it is a grand mixture of mysticism and what its author sincerely believed to be cold, sober scientific fact. Naturally, he believed that he was being persecuted by orthodoxy, and that all official scientists were his personal enemies, so that it was a little difficult to argue with him. From his own point of view, he was unlucky not to live long enough to see the remarkable rise to favour of WEL (*Welt Eis Lehre*, or Cosmic Ice Theory) under the Nazis.

According to Hörbiger, and to his disciple H.S. Bellamy, practically everything in the universe, apart from the Earth and the Sun, is made up of ice. The stars are ice-blocks, and so they are freezing cold instead of boiling hot. The planet Mars has an icy coating 250 miles deep, and the Martian canals are simply cracks in the surface (it was not until much later that the canals were, alas, found to be due to nothing more than tricks of the eye). The Moon is equally icy, and the same is true of all the other members of the Solar System, so that the universe is a distinctly chilly place.

Next we come to space itself, which, according to Hörbiger and Bellamy, is filled with rarefied hydrogen. Now any gas, however thin, will set up a certain amount of resistance to any object ploughing through it, and Hörbiger claimed that this resistance would slow a planet down. The effect would admittedly be slight, but over the centuries it would mount up. Therefore, each planet will spiral steadily down towards the Sun, as will the minor members of the Solar System such as asteroids and meteoroids. When one of these ice-blocks falls into the Sun, it produces a sunspot before being unceremoniously snuffed out.

This will also be the fate of the Earth. Eventually, as the steady drag caused by the hydrogen begins to overcome our orbital motion, the world will approach the Sun, and even before it is vaporised it will drop on to the solar surface, producing a particularly large sunspot. To the disciples of WEL, this is a fate which cannot be avoided, though they did admit that it is not imminent, mainly because the Earth is unique in being devoid of an icy shell.

However, a more pressing danger comes from the Moon, which also is being braked by the hydrogen, and is spiralling down towards us. It is not the first Moon. In previous times the Earth has had at least six others, all of which were composed of ice, and all of which were torn apart by the strong pull of gravity as they swung dangerously close. Every time an ice-Moon is disrupted there are violent cataclysms, and one of these dates back to about 65 million years ago. As the ice-Moon spiralled inward, braked remorselessly by the rarefied hydrogen through which it had to batter its way, it pulled our seas up into a kind of girdle round the equator. Because of the approach of so large a piece of ice, the Earth's temperature dropped disastrously, and terrified humanity had to retreat to the areas which were climatically the least unpleasant. Still the ice-Moon swung inward, until it dominated the entire sky and gave rise to folk-legends of dragons and evil spirits. Finally there came the great cataclysm. The ice-Moon was broken up by the powerful gravity of the Earth, and literally disintegrated. Ice rained down upon the surface of our world, followed by rocks and all manner of miscellaneous debris. The Earth, which had been twisted out of shape, reverted to its original spherical form with devastating suddenness. Earthquakes and violent eruptions followed; the equatorial waters flowed back to higher latitudes, and, needless to say, produced the Biblical Flood.

Bellamy (who took over where Hörbiger left off) calculated that our present Moon was captured by the Earth about 13,000 years ago, and is now drawing steadily closer and closer. Finally it will come within what is known as the Roche limit, and disaster will follow. This limit, named after the nineteenth-century French mathematician Edouard Roche, who was the first to describe it, may be called the danger zone round the Earth, where the gravitational pull is so strong that any fragile body will be disrupted (this does not apply to a structure such as a space station, which is of rigid construction). The Roche limit lies about 5,700 miles above the ground, so that our present Moon is well beyond it.

However, again citing Bellamy, the hydrogen braking will go remorselessly on. The Moon will come nearer and nearer until it looms in the sky as a large, terrifying body, causing tremendous tides that will flood most of the continents. Then the earthquakes will start; the lands will twist and writhe as though in agony, and the tilt of the axis will be altered, so that the climates will change too. We may imagine polar bears striding through the present-day

Sahara, while rhinoceroses and hippopotami will make for the sunnier climes of Greenland or Antarctica. Men will face a crisis, and not many of the human race will survive. Will this be the end? Not really – at least, Bellamy didn't think so. When the Moon comes within the Roche limit it will shatter into frozen fragments, and these will rain down on the Earth, so that going for an afternoon walk will involve the serious risk of being hit on the head by a tumbling ice-block. At last the supply of fragments will be exhausted; the Earth will 'snap back' into its previous state, and a new era will begin, to last until we capture another ice-Moon and the story is repeated. The end will come with the arrival of a more massive Moon, which will shatter the world into tiny pieces.

There are a few Independent Thinkers who achieve not only fame, but also some degree of official backing. Dr Velikovsky, to be discussed in the next chapter, was one. Another was Trofim Lysenko, a Russian student of evolution and heredity, whose peculiar theories were supported by the Soviet Government to the exclusion of all others, and who managed to put back the study of genetics in the USSR by at least thirty years; even now it has not fully recovered, though Lysenko has long since fallen from grace (he died in 1976). And the WEL cult, which was just as outlandish as anything that Velikovsky or Lysenko could conjure up, was backed quite seriously by the Nazis in Germany before World War II; at one stage the Government even had to issue an official statement to the effect that one could still be a good National Socialist without believing in cosmic ice! Moreover, there was one famous astronomer, Philip Fauth, who drew a large if inaccurate lunar map and became something of a convert, effectively ruining his scientific reputation in the process.

At its height, WEL probably had as many as a million supporters, most of them in Germany but quite a few in other countries as well, including England. After World War

II, with the advent of space travel, it inevitably declined, and when Neil Armstrong took his famous 'one small step' on to the lunar Sea of Tranquillity without finding the need to equip himself with skates, the idea of an icy Moon died. Yet there are still some people who accept the theory that the Earth is spiralling towards destruction, and will come to an end when it makes its final dive into the solar flames.

In fact the Earth's path round the Sun is absolutely stable, so let us return to the Moon. Here we find a different situation. Instead of approaching us, the Moon is moving further away. The recession is not great, and amounts to only a few centimetres per year, but it brings us back to the whole idea of tidal friction and the Moon's trick of keeping the same face turned towards us all the time.

The Moon's revolution period round the Earth is 27.3 days. (To be pedantic, this is the time taken for the Earth and Moon to revolve round their common centre of gravity, but this point lies inside the Earth's globe, so for the moment we need not bother about it.) The axial rotation period of the Moon is also 27.3 days. This is really too much to be coincidental, and there is no mystery about it. Long ago, when the Solar System was young, the Moon is thought to have spun round much more quickly, but it was strongly affected by the gravitational pull of the Earth, which tended to cause a bulge in the Moon's still-viscous globe. As the Moon rotated, it had to fight against this force, and its spin was slowed down until, relative to the Earth, it had stopped altogether. The lunar rotation had become synchronous or 'captured'.

Note that I say that the rotation had stopped 'relative to the Earth', which is not the same thing as saying that it had stopped altogether. Relative to the Sun, the Moon continues to spin round, so that day and night conditions are the same all over the surface; once the Sun rises over any particular region, it will not set again for a period equal to two terrestrial weeks, which is something that future colonists will find rather strange. Years ago I gave an analogy, which I repeat here because I have never been able to think of anything better. Take a chair to represent the Earth, and let your head represent the Moon; your face is the familiar hemisphere, while the back of your head is 'the other side'. Now look at the chair and walk round it, turning as you go so as to keep your face turned chairward. After one circuit you will have faced every wall of the room, so that you will have turned once on your axis, but anyone sitting on the chair will never have seen the back of your neck. This is how the Moon behaves, and this is why we Earthbound mortals are permanently unable to see the far hemisphere.

(I admit that there are certain complications, and the Moon seems to rock very slowly to and fro, so that all in all we can examine a grand total of 59 per cent of the total surface; only 41 per cent is permanently out of view, but this is something which need not bother us now, because the basic principle is clear enough.)

There is another point to bear in mind. Just as the Earth slowed down the spin of the Moon, so the Moon is doing its best to retard the spin of the Earth. It is, of course, the chief tide-producing agent, and the friction of the water against the sea-bed has a definite effect. The days are getting longer. Not by much; neglecting random variations, each day is 0.00000002 seconds longer than its predecessor, which adds up to about one-fiftieth of a second every 1,000 years. You might think that this would be undetectable, but nowadays we have atomic clocks which are better timekeepers than the Earth. We can also see the effects when we come to study eclipse records of long ago.

Consider eclipses of the Sun. These occur when the new moon passes directly in front of the Sun, hiding it briefly; by a lucky chance (and here we really do have to assume that it is sheer coincidence) the Moon and the Sun appear about the same size in the sky, so that under suitable conditions the Moon can blot out the Sun completely. These solar eclipses were recorded by all the early peoples, and caused considerable alarm. The Chinese believed that a hungry dragon was trying to gobble up the Sun, which would certainly mean the end of the world; the obvious remedy was to shout, scream, beat gongs and drums, and make as much commotion as possible in order to scare the beast away. (It always worked, though there is a story, probably apocryphal, that two Court astrologers with the unlikely names of Hsi and Ho were executed because they had failed to predict an eclipse, thereby imperilling the Emperor and everybody else.) The Greeks were more scientific, and they timed the eclipses quite well. Working backwards, it is found that their timings do not agree with what might be expected, and this brings us back to the increase in the length of the day.

Are you ready for a little mathematics? I hope so, and I promise that it involves nothing more fearsome than simple multiplication and division. If you are as bad at mathematics as I am, you may skip the next paragraph, but I would urge you to try to follow me.

Each day is 0.00000002 seconds longer than the previous one. Therefore, a century ago (that is to say 36,525 days ago) the length of the day was shorter by 0.00073 seconds. Taking an average between then and now, the length of the day was half this value, or 0.00036 seconds shorter than at present. But since 36,525 days have elapsed, the total error is 36,525 x 0.00036 = 13 seconds. Thefore, when we calculate back, the position of the Moon will be in error; it will seem to have moved too far, i.e. too fast. The discrepancy shows up when we consider eclipses which took place in classical times. Astronomers call it 'secular acceleration', and find that the difference between observation and calculation can amount to several hours. Moreover, eclipse records go back a long way. For instance, one was described in the inscription on a clay tablet found in the ruins of the ancient seaport of Ugarit, in what is now Syria. This eclipse happened in 1375 BC.

It is also known that the loss of energy caused by the slowing down of the Earth is transferred to the Moon, which is why the Moon is edging outwards. Calculating forwards now instead of backwards, we find that in about the year AD 50,000 million the Moon will have receded to 340,000 miles; it will then take 47 days to go round us, and this will also be the length of the Earth's axial rotation, so that inhabitants of one hemisphere will find the Moon permanently above the horizon, while dwellers in the other hemisphere will never see it at all.

But now a new factor emerges. The Moon is not the only tide-raiser; the Sun has an effect as well, and when the Moon has reached its maximum distance from us the solar tides will go on slowing down the Earth's spin. Everything is reversed. When the Earth's rotation has become longer than the Moon's revolution period, the Moon will start to come inwards again. Inexorably the approach will continue, until at last the Moon comes within the Roche limit, and is broken up by the Earth's gravity. It will shatter, first into large pieces and then into smaller ones; these remnants will be spread round the Earth, so that instead of having a large satellite we will have a system of rings. Even before this, huge tides will have swept over the lands, wiping out all life, while the crust of the Earth itself will have been breached. If the Moon is not disrupted, it will coincide with the Earth and destroy both bodies, leaving nothing but a swarm of debris.

All this sounds plausible enough, and has been the subject of many technical investigations, but we now know that it can never happen, because the timescale is completely wrong. So far as we are concerned there can never be a year AD 50,000 million, because the Earth will not then exist;

it will have been destroyed by changes in the energy output of the Sun, to be described in Chapter 10.

What, then, are the chances of a wandering body invading the Earth – Moon system, wrenching the Moon out of its stable orbit and sending it crashing Earthwards? Again we must say that this is absolutely out of the question, and so the Moon is no threat. There have been some vastly entertaining stories about lunar collisions, notably R.C. Sheriff's The Hopkins Manuscript and Olaf Stapledon's classic Last and First Men, but they are fiction only, and have no scientific basis.

Yet the fears linger on. Not many years ago there was a minor panic in Brazil, caused by a radio announcer who had been dismissed for some reason or other, and who was feeling decidedly peeved with the authorities. When reading his final news bulletin, he calmly stated that astronomers had made a great discovery: the Moon was falling, and was due to land on the Earth within a couple of weeks. Quite a number of listeners believed him, and the radio station was besieged by callers who wanted to know what was the best course of action. I understand that the announcer became somewhat unpopular with his superiors, and this was definitely his last broadcast; but he had made his point, and for some weeks afterwards there were many Brazilians who kept their eyes turned skywards, hoping against hope that the Moon would not swell in size prior to landing in the jungle with an unpleasant thud.

Comets of Doom

I have already mentioned Comet Hale-Bopp, which graced our skies in 1997; it was brighter than Hyakutake, the comet of the previous year. It inspired affection rather than terror, and I think everyone was sorry to see it go – but at least we can look out for it again in 2,400 years' time.

However, things were very different in 1973. Early in that year Dr Lubos Kohoutek, an eminent Czech astronomer who was then working at the Hamburg Observatory in West Germany, discovered a comet. This, in the normal way, would not have been remarkable. Several comets are under observation every year, some of them bright enough to be seen in telescopes of moderate size; a new discovery is interesting, but in the ordinary course of events it provokes no discussion outside astronomical circles. However, Kohoutek's Comet was different. Though it looked like nothing more than a tiny smudge on the photograph plate, its movement showed that it was a very long way away. Its distance from us was over 400 million miles, and few comets are visible as far out in the Solar System as that.

Therefore the comet was large, and when its orbit was worked out even non-astronomers started to become excited. Calculations showed that in November the comet's orbit would cross that of the Earth, though the Earth itself would be nowhere near the point of intersection and no collision would be possible. Predictions indicated that before the beginning of December we would be treated to a real spectacle – a comet almost as bright as the half-Moon, with a tail stretching across the sky in the manner of a scimitar. At its perihelion, or closest approach to the Sun, it would be racing along at about 100 miles per second (as against the Earth's sluggish 18.5 miles per second), and in the middle of January 1974 it would brush past us at only 75 million miles, still brilliant and imposing. Well before it drew close to the Earth's orbit it had been nicknamed 'the Comet of the Century'.

Alas, no astronomer is infallible, and comets are never reliable. Kohoutek's Comet moved exactly as forecast, but as a spectacle it proved to be a non-event. At its best it was visible with the naked eye if you knew where to look for it, but that was all, and I had every sympathy with my old friend Bernard Levin, who wrote a bitter letter in the London *Times* accusing me of having stolen the comet for reasons of my own! People who had expected a display of cosmic pyrotechnics were sadly disappointed.

I mention Kohoutek's Comet because at the time when it was drawing inwards, and was still expected to become brilliant, astrologers and other end-of-the-worlders were in full cry. For instance, there was a lurid pamphlet entitled *The Christmas Monster*, written by Mr Moses David and issued by a religious organisation calling itself the Children of God, about whom I have no further information. The comet, wrote Mr David, was a sign of divine vengeance. Even if the world did not actually perish, there would be widespread damage, with storms, tempests and tremendous earthquakes. He also claimed that it would mark the downfall of 'Fascist America and its new Nazi Emperor'. Presumably he and his followers were somewhat chagrined when the comet turned out to be so puny, and natural disasters were conspicuous only by their absence.

Comets have always been regarded as unlucky, and the fear of them is not completely dead even yet, as Mr David's pamphlet showed. They have been responsible for several panics in historical times, and they were generally taken to be signs of divine displeasure. Basically, there are four causes of apprehension: nebulous fears of the astrological type, the destruction of the Earth by a head-on collision, a near miss which would tip the world sideways or else throw it out of its present orbit, and contamination of the atmosphere by poisonous cometary gases.

Ancient peoples had no idea of the true nature of comets, and tended to regard them as luminous phenomena in the upper air, but certainly they had an intense distrust of them. The Romans were of this opinion. I quote Tacitus, writing in AD 64: 'At the close of this year people discoursed only of prodigies, the forerunners of approaching calamities; of thunderstorms more frequent than at any other epoch, and of a comet, a kind of presage that Nero always expiated with illustrious blood.' The Emperor Nero, who was ruler of Rome at the time, was not noted for his kindness and generosity; his reign was punctuated by several comets, so that historians such as Tacitus drew their own conclusions. Later, in AD 79, another bright comet appeared, but the current Emperor, Vespasian, was not alarmed: 'This hairy star does not concern me. It menaces rather the King of the Parthians, for he is hairy, while I am bald.' Alas, Vespasian was wrong. He died soon after the comet had faded from the sky.

All this is not the same as possible global destruction, but the overall fear of comets persisted for a long time. One famous description was given by the French doctor Ambroise Pare in 1528:

This comet was so horrible, so frightful, and it produced such great terror that some died of fright and others fell sick. It appeared to be of extreme length, and was the colour of blood. At the summit of it was seen the figure of a bent arm, holding in its hand a great sword as though about to strike. At the end of the point there were three stars. On both sides of the rays of this comet there were seen a great number of axes, knives and blood-coloured swords, among which were a large number of hideous human faces, with beards and bristling hair.

Whether Dr Pare was actually describing a comet is not certain; he may have seen a brilliant display of aurora borealis or northern lights, and it is true that there are no other records of a comet in 1528, but it demonstrates the fear which comets inspired.

In Shakespeare's Julius Caesar we find the famous lines:

When beggars die, there are no comets seen;
The heavens themselves blaze forth the death of princes.

While Milton, in Paradise Lost, wrote:

Satan stood
Unterrified, and like a comet burn'd
That fires the length of Ophiuchus huge
In th'Artick sky, and from its horrid hair
Shakes pestilence and war.

Yet are there any scientific grounds for the dread of comets, and what would happen if we really did suffer a direct collision?

Brilliant though they may sometimes become, comets are flimsy, ethereal things. A large comet is made up of a nucleus, surrounded by a head or coma, and with a tail (or tails) streaming outwards. Most of the mass is concentrated in the nucleus, which is thought to be icy in nature, composed of what may be termed an icy conglomerate – that is to say, small solid particles held together in ices such as those of frozen ammonia, methane, carbon dioxide and water. Comets have been likened to dirty ice-balls, which may be unromantic but is certainly apt. Tails are of two main kinds: those composed of gas, and those which are made up of dust. In general the gas-tails are straight, the dust-tails curved; many large comets have both (Hale-Bopp did). These tails always point more or less away from the Sun, because they are repelled by the 'solar wind', a stream of low-energy atomic particles being sent out from the Sun in all directions, and by the actual pressure of sunlight. Therefore, when a comet is receding from the Sun it travels tail-first.

Not all comets have tails. Most of them look more like tiny pieces of luminous cotton wool in the sky, with no definite shape at all, and because they depend upon reflected sunlight they can be seen only when they are reasonably close to the Sun and the Earth. (As they near perihelion, they do emit a certain amount of light on their own account, but even so the Sun is directly responsible.) Cometary gas is extremely thin, and is millions of times less dense than the air that you and I are breathing, so that it can do us no harm, even though some of its constituents would be poisonous in greater quantity. Only the nucleus is dense enough to do damage, and it must be admitted that as yet our positive knowledge of cometary nuclei is very incomplete.

Most comets move round the Sun in very elliptical paths. Those which have periods of a few years must be regarded as old friends, and we always know when and where to expect them. Thus Encke's Comet (named after the nineteenth-century German astronomer Johann Encke, who was the first to work out its orbit) has a period of only 33 years, and has now been seen at over fifty different returns. But with one exception, Halley's, all the short-period or medium-period comets are faint, and the brilliant visitors seen now and then take so long to complete one journey round the Sun that they cannot be predicted. They were fairly frequent during the nineteenth century, but since then there has been a relative dearth of them. Of course, many of the fainter comets are also to all intents and purposes non-periodical, and Kohoutek's, for example, is not expected back for about 75,000 years. Meanwhile, there has been a recent theory due to two eminent astronomers, Victor Clube and Bill Napier, which is relevant here, and is as unexpected as it is fascinating.

Most astronomers believe that comets are bona fide members of the Solar System, and were produced from the 'solar nebula', a cloud of material associated with the youthful Sun. Clube and Napier do not agree. They think that comets are collected by the Sun during its passage through a vast interstellar cloud, so that there are definite epochs when the supply of comets is replenished. This is logical enough, because even though there are plenty of comets around at the present time, they must be short-lived on the cosmical scale. Each time a comet nears the Sun it is heated, and some of its ices are evaporated to form the tail, so that after a definite number of returns to perihelion all the gas is exhausted; nothing remains but the nucleus, and according to one theory the comet then becomes an asteroid or minor planet. This is not to suggest that all asteroids are ex-comets; some of them are far too large and massive – Ceres, the senior member of the swarm, has a diameter of over 580 miles. However, those asteroids which swing away from the main zone between

Mars and Jupiter are in a different category, and I will have more to say about them later.

Clube and Napier have made exhaustive studies of old legends and myths, and believe that in the remote past a brilliant periodical comet, named by them the Cosmic Serpent, made periodical close approaches to the Earth. Parts of it broke away and landed, causing wide devastation. If this is correct, it would at least go a long way towards explaining the age-old fear of comets. Finally the Cosmic Serpent disintegrated; many other periodical comets collected by the Sun during its last passage through an interstellar cloud, ending about 10,000 years ago, have also disappeared, so that the total number of Solar System comets will not be restored until the next crossing of a cloud.

It is fair to say that many people are somewhat dubious about the theory, but it must be taken very seriously. A direct hit from a large comet-turned-asteroid might well fracture the earth's crust. Luckily, the odds against such a collision are very great.

The most famous of all comets is named in honour of Edmond Halley, a close friend of Isaac Newton, who became the second Astronomer Royal at Greenwich. Halley saw the comet in 1682, when it was a prominent naked-eye object, and found that its orbit was remarkably similar to those of comets seen previously in 1607 and in 1531. He reasoned that the three comets must be one and the same, with a period of seventy-six years, and he predicted that it would be seen once more in 1758. It was; on Christmas night of that year it was picked up by a Saxon amateur named Palitzsch, and since then it has been back three times. It was spectacular in 1835 and in 1910, but at the last return, that of 1986, it was as badly placed as it could possibly be, and from the point of view of the general public was disappointing. It will not be any better in 2061. But look out for it in 2137 – it will be truly magnificent.

It was during Edmond Halley's time that we come to the greatest of all comet scares. The man responsible, the Revd William Whiston, had made his reputation as a serious scientist, and when he published his remarkable book *A New Theory of the Earth*, in 1696, he was not howled down. The book was well received, and ran to several editions. Seven years later Whiston was appointed Lucasian Professor of Mathematics at Cambridge in succession to Newton, so that at that stage he can hardly have been regarded as an eccentric.

Whiston was born in 1667 in the village of Norton-juxta-Twycrosse, in Leicestershire. From all accounts his upbringing was extremely strict, since his father and all the members of his family were highly religious, and prayers and sermons continued for much of the day and night. Young Whiston may have been melancholy and neurotic, but he was academically brilliant, and when he went to Cambridge University at the age of nineteen he soon earned a reputation as an excellent mathematician. (Later on he carried out some valuable researches, particularly in connection with the exact determination of longitude.) He graduated from Cambridge with honours, and in 1693 he was ordained, becoming Chaplain to Bishop Moore of Norwich. He was also made Vicar of Lowestoft-with-Kissingland at the munificent salary of £120 per year, and resigned only when he became Lucasian Professor in 1703. There seemed no reason whatsoever why he should not live out his life as a respected and serious academic.

Yet his *New Theory of the Earth* was not only unconventional, but wildly so, and he made the classic mistake of confusing comets with planets. He went so far as to claim that the Earth used to be a comet with a path which took it close to the Sun, so that the present heat of the Earth's core is an aftermath of the high temperatures to which our luckless world was subjected during its cometary phase. When

God decided that the time had come for Man to appear, the comet's path became less eccentric, so that the air was purified, oceans appeared, and the Earth changed from a comet into a planet...

Even though comets were still regarded as mysterious objects at that period, it is hard to understand why this book was taken seriously. It was obvious, particularly to Newton and Halley, that the difference in mass between a comet and a planet is so vast that there can be no interchange of identity. True, comets may be large – the coma of the great comet of 1843, for instance, was bigger than the Sun – but by planetary standards their masses are absolutely negligible; it is rather like comparing a meringue with a cannonball. There have been observational proofs of this in more recent times. In 1770 Lexell's Comet, admittedly one of the smaller specimens, passed within 750,000 miles of the Earth, so that it was visible with the naked eye, and the French mathematician Laplace pointed out that if the comet had been as massive as the Earth, our 'day' would have been shortened by almost three hours. Of course there was no effect at all, and Laplace found that the mass of the comet could not have been more than 1/5000 of that of the Earth (actually it was much less than that). Subsequently, Lexell's Comet had the temerity to approach mighty Jupiter, and invaded the Jovian satellite system. Neither Jupiter nor its moons showed any effects, but the comet's orbit was so violently twisted that it was completely changed, and astronomers lost track of it. No doubt the comet still exists, but we have no idea where it is now.

Quite apart from this fundamental error, Whiston's theories were hardly scientific. He concentrated upon a bright comet which had been seen in 1680, and to which Edmond Halley (wrongly) assigned a period of 575 years. God, said Whiston, had always had an uneasy feeling that

Man might be prone to sin, and so he had fashioned the 1680 comet as an agent of punishment. Indeed, it had aleady been in action: on either 28 November 1349 BC or 2 December 2926 BC, the comet approached the Earth, and by-passed us within 9,000 miles. Assuming that the comet had a mass one-quarter that of the Earth (!), Whiston claimed that the effect was to produce a huge tide not only in the oceans, but also in the lands. Water swirled around, mountains were broken apart, and much of the world was covered by a flood more than six miles deep, so that almost every man, woman and beast came to an untimely end. Need I add that this was nothing more nor less than the Biblical Deluge? The head and tail of the rampaging comet actually struck the Earth, and discharged so much water that rain kept on falling for forty days and forty nights. Finally God decided that since there were so few people left – only Noah and his nearest and dearest – it might be as well to give Homo sapiens a second chance. The comet receded, the water-level fell, and the Earth became habitable again; the doors of the Ark opened, and the situation reverted to normal.

Unfortunately Man had not learned his lesson. Before long there was new evidence of sin, and the comet was still lurking in the background, ready for further onslaught if need be. Whiston held that it would soon come back, and that this time there would be no half-measures. The best description I have found was given later by the French astronomer Pingre, and it is worth quoting here, because it is so vivid:

> Hardly can the mouth of a volcano vomiting forth lava liquefied by the interior consuming heat give an idea of the fiery atmosphere of the comet. The air will then interpose no obstacle to the activity of this central fire; on the contrary, the inflamed particles with which our atmosphere will be

charged, carried down by their own weight into the half-open
bowels of the Earth, will powerfully augment the action of the
central fire. The comet will even separate the Moon from the
Earth, and affect the diurnal and annual motion of the Earth
by rendering both these movements equal, and by destroying
besides the eccentricity of the Earth's orbit, which will again
become circlar as before the Flood. Lastly, after the saints have
reigned a thousand years on Earth, itself regenerated by fire
and rendered habitable anew by Divine will, the comet will
again strike the Earth, the terrestrial orbit will be excessively
elongated, and the Earth, once more a comet, will cease to be
habitable.

This did not sound at all promising, but Whiston was
confident that there could be no mistake. The only point
at issue was – when? 1715 was one possibility, but when
that year passed by with no alarms or excursions Whiston
checked his calculations and found that the end would
certainly come in 1736.

Meanwhile his own career had taken a turn for the
worse, not because of his preoccupation with the comet
but for much more immediate reasons. His religious views
were not conventional, and in 1708 he was accused of
Arianism. Few people will know what Arianism is (I didn't,
until I looked it up). It is, in fact, an early theological
heresy, teaching that God is utterly isolated and separated
from the beings he has created. Whiston was violently
attacked by his clerical colleagues but, being Whiston, he
declined to retract. Instead he published a book called
Primitive Christianity Reviewed, which only made matters
worse. Inevitably, he was asked to resign as Lucasian
Professor, and when he refused to do so he was dismissed.
He was even prosecuted for heresy, and though nothing
came of it he retired in dudgeon to a farm in Suffolk,
where he continued both his useful scientific work and

his calculations about the approach Day of Judgement in which his faith never wavered.

Eventually he seems to have decided that the end would come on 16 October 1736. He predicted that a comet would appear (not the 1680 one, presumably, but another dispatched specifically for the purpose); the Second Coming would be timed for the previous day, and the final destruction would be in a holocaust of fire and brimstone. At this stage the story becomes rather confused. There are reports that three days before his scheduled Day of Doom he gave a public lecture in London in which he broadcast his warning, allowing his hearers sufficient time to repent. Certainly there was something of a local panic; people started streaming out of the city, though just why they should have regarded the surrounding countryside as safer is not clear. It is even on record that the Archbishop of Canterbury felt bound to issue a public disclaimer.

I have been unable to find any really reliable reports of what went on, and the terror was short-lived. The Day of Judgement was again postponed, Whiston went back to Suffolk, and that was that. Whiston lived on until 1752, still confident that the comet would return. Nowadays it is thought that the commet of 1680 has a period of at least 8,000 years, in which case we have a long reprieve.

You might imagine that the idea of comets changing into planets, or vice versa, would have died with Whiston. Not so! In 1950 there came *Worlds in Collision*, by a Russian-born, American-based psychoanalyst named Immanuel Velikovsky, which was decidedly Whistonian in character. This time the planet Jupiter suffered a tremendous outburst, and expelled a comet, which subsequently turned into the planet Venus. Initially it bounced around the cosmos rather in the manner of a celestial ping-pong ball, and it had several traumatic

encounters with the Earth. One of these occurred when
the Israelites were crossing the Red Sea. The pull of
the comet stopped the Earth's rotation at a convenient
moment, and allowed the party to cross from one shore to
the other without getting their feet wet. Later the comet
returned, showering down the manna which provided
enough food to last for forty years. It then had a near-
encounter with Mars, and had its tail chopped off; Mars
itself approached the Earth, and scored a near miss in 687
BC. Various other encounters took place, suitably linked
with events in the Old Testament, and so on.

All this is great fun, and the Biblical references are
absolutely correct. Neither could there be any doubt about
Velikovsky's sincerity. He became something of a cult figure
in the United States, and amassed a considerable following.
But to the best of my knowledge he never gave a definite
date for the end of the world, so that he does not concern
us further here.

Going back in time once more, we come to the year
1773, and a paper by the great French mathematician
Lalande called (in translation) 'Reflections on those
Comets which can approach the Earth'. Lalande's paper
sparked off a curious panic which affected not only Paris,
but also much of France. According to rumour, a comet
would collide with the Earth on 20 or 21 May, with
cataclysmic results. Lalande had not, of course, suggested
anything of the kind, so by early May he felt compelled
to issue a clarification, but his letter, published in the
Gazette de France, had an effect opposite to what had been
intended; many people jumped to the conclusion that he
was trying to hide the truth. One man who was not taken
in was the famous writer Francois-Marie Arouet Voltaire,
who set to work and produced a Letter on the Pretended
Comet, which appeared on 17 May. In it he commented
that 'certain Parisians ... expect a comet, which is to take

our little globe from behind and reduce it to impalpable powder, according to a certain prediction of the Academy of Sciences, which has not yet been made'. But 'the Parisians will not desert their city on 20 May; they still sing their songs, and the play *The Comet and the End of the World* will be performed at the Opera-Comique'.

Yet the alarm spread, and some members of the clergy took advantage of it. They announced that they had been allotted preferential tickets for seats in Paradise, and proceeded to sell them at high prices. I am not sure how many were sold, but it must have been a considerable number. History does not relate whether any of the buyers subsequently got their money back.

France was again the scene of the next comet scare, which occurred in 1832. This time the culprit was a comet which later became notorious for an entirely different reason. It had originally been found in 1772 by Charles Messier, who was one of the most successful of all comet hunters, and who made many discoveries, though he is best remembered today for his catalogue of star-clusters and the misty-looking objects which we term nebulae and galaxies. The comet was not brilliant, but it was easy to locate, and its orbit was calculated by a German named Friedrich Bessel, who found that it had a period of 6¾ years. The next few years passed unnoticed, but Bessel predicted that the comet would be seen again in 1826, and on 27 February that year it was picked up by an Austrian soldier, Captain Wilhelm von Biela, who was a skilful amateur astronomer. We remember it today as Biela's Comet.

The next return was scheduled for 1832, and in France yet another eminent mathematician, Damoiseau, found that its orbit would cut that of the Earth on 29 October. He was quite right, but the repercussions were startling. Once more the alarm was spread; newspaper headlines proclaimed that the Earth would be smashed into tiny fragments, and that there was little what anyone could do about it.

There was, however, one fact which the newspapers had overlooked, but which was pointed out by Francois Arago, the leading French astronomer of the time. Certainly the orbit of Biela's Comet would intersect that of the Earth – but the Earth would be nowhere near the cutting-point at the time. Arago found that the minimum distance between the Earth and the comet would be over 49 million miles. But things were by now out of control, and according to a later account, written by an author named Mackay, 'the greatest alarm spread over the continent of Europe, lest the comet, whose appearance was then foretold by astronomers, should destroy the Earth. Many persons refrained from undertaking or concluding any business during that year.'

Beila's Comet came and went without incident. It was missed at the return of 1839, because it was unfavourably placed for observation; at its return in 1846 it split in two parts, and the twins came back once more in 1852, but that was their swan-song. They have never been seen since, though their remnants have been observed in the form of a show of meteors or shooting-stars. Other old periodical comets have vanished just as effectively, but Biela's is the classic case of a comet death.

I have already mentioned the great comet of 1843, which was really brilliant, and which appeared at the climax of the Millerite scare, though William Miller himself had not necessarily expected it, and had relied entirely upon his Biblical calculations. Then, in 1857, a German writer whose name I have failed to unearth announced that a fiery comet would destroy the world on 13 June; there were various apprehensive comments, but, predictably, nothing happened. Four years later the

Earth passed harmlessly through the tail of a great comet, but the only visible result was a slight luminosity of the sky on the night of 30 June 1861, and even this rests upon very uncertain evidence. The distance between the Earth and the comet's head was about 11 million miles, so that the danger was nil.

There was yet another 'comet scare' in France in 1857, caused this time not by a brilliant visitor, but by a comet which never appeared at all. It was sparked off, quite unintentionally, by two reputable astronomers, Richard Dunthorne in England and A. Pingre in France. Dunthorne calculated the orbits of the bright comets seen in 1264 and 1566, and came to the conclusion that they might be identical. Accordingly, Pingre predicted a return for about 1848. Subsequently, he revised this to some time between 1856 and 1860, because of the gravitational effects of Saturn and Neptune, which had not previously been taken into account.

This was by no means sensational; but then a German astrologer, whose name has not only come back in 1857, but would collide with the Earth on 13 June. For some reason or other panic started, confined mainly though not entirely in Paris. A correspondent there wrote that 'For a fortnight we have not been able to step out without hearing the cry, "Here is the end of the World! A full description of the comet of June 13!" Women have miscarried; crops have been neglected; a cometary life insurance company (premiums payable in advance) was set up ...' Prophets of doom were much in evidence. Not everyone took it seriously; there was a superb series of cartoons on the subject by the caricaturist Honore Daumier, and leading astronomers of the time were not impressed. But not until 13 June was well past did the panic die away. Actually no bright comet appeared in 1857; 1858 saw the visit of Donati's Comet, which, with its magnificent tails, was possibly the most beautiful ever observed, but this time nobody in Paris was alarmed.

Halley's Comet returned in 1910, and made a brave showing. True, it was not so brilliant as the 'Daylight Comet', which had been on view a few weeks earlier; this was truly magnificent, and, as its nickname suggests, was visible with the naked eye even when the Sun was well above the horizon. (Do not wait for it to come back; its orbital period is of the order of 4 million years.) Halley's Comet caused a great deal of interest, mixed with some alarm. There was no suggestion that it would hit the Earth, but it was predicted that on the night of 18 May 1910 the Earth would pass through the comet's tail, and it was this which caused misgivings. Comet tails contain the deadly gas cyanogens; could we be damaged? In the United States one prestigious paper, the *Boston Herald*, carried a headline *COMET'S TAIL IS POISON: Astronomers Believe It May Snuff Out Life on Earth*. And even the eminent French astronomer Camille Flammarion went on record as saying that the danger was very real. On the night of 18 May there were signs of alarm everywhere – and not only in America. Many people did their best to seal their doors and windows so as to keep out the cyanogens, while one enterprising gentleman in New York made a large sum of money by selling what he called 'comet pills'. Just exactly what these pills were meant to do has never been made clear.

Actually, the density of the gas in a comet's tail is so low – millions of times more rarefied than the air we breath – that even it if were composed of pure cyanogens it could do us no harm. Halley's Comet departed, not to return for another seventy-six years, and everybody went back to work.

There was a minor disturbance in 1944 in South America, when a Chilean astronomer named Munos Ferradas announced that a comet would strike the Earth some time in August of that year. People in both Chile and Bolivia made for the hills, and stayed there until they were satisfied that the danger had passed. In fact no major comet was seen at any time in 1944, or for some years afterwards, though Arend-Roland of 1957 and Ikeya-Seki of 1966 became quite prominent, and in 1970 another naked-eye visitor, Comet Bennett, was believed by some Arabs to be an Israeli war weapon.

Came 1986 – and with it, once more, Halley's Comet. It was not nearly so bright as it had been in 1835 or 1910, because it was badly placed in the sky, and there seem to have been no really major panics associated with it, though of course the astrologers made all sorts of dire predictions. It was, however, a very important return scientifically, because for the first time it was possible to send up rocket probes. The European spacecraft Giotto actually penetrated the comet's head, and sent back the first close-range images of the nucleus, which turned out to be encrusted with dark material; it was lozenge-shaped, with a longest diameter of just under ten miles, and was composed chiefly of water ice. It would take 60,000 million comets of this mass to equal the mass of the Earth.

As an aside, I cannot resist recalling the Halley's Comet Society, which was founded mainly by my old friend Brian Harpur. Generally speaking, the Society had no aims, no objectives and no ambitions; all it did was to meet occasionally on licensed premises. We did, however, hold one major concert, at Wembley, with all the proceeds devoted to charity. (My personal contribution was limited mainly to playing a xylophone solo.) Just before 'curtain up' a procession marched by, bearing placards such as REPENT: THE HOUR OF DOOM IS AT HAND. Evidently the comet was believed to be responsible, but just what was expected to happen we never found out, and the concert went ahead as planned. Yet on balance, it is fair to say that the Halley's Comet Society is the only completely useless society in the world, apart of course from the European Parliament.

Colin Ronan, one of our leading members, was always adamant that 'Halley' should be pronounced 'Hawley', which may be true, and in the Society we always deferred to his opinion. This led to the modification of an old rhyme, dating back to around 1910.

> Of all the comets in the sky,
> There's none like Comet Halley.
> We see it with the naked eye,
> And periodically.

John Mason produced his own version:

> Of all the comets in the sky,
> There's none like Comet Hawley.
> We saw it with the naked eye,
> But this time – rather poorly.

Yet the last word had not been said, and in 1994 an unusual advertisement appeared in many daily papers, including the Guardian. They had been placed by one Sofia Richmond (real name Sofia Segatis Paprocki Orvid Piciato), who hailed from Poland, but lived in Cricklewood in London. Apparently she regarded herself as a saint who had been sent to warn the world of impending disaster. Her main theme was that following some sort of explosion beyond the orbit of Jupiter, Halley's Comet had turned round and was heading towards us, with potentially disastrous results. I quote from her advertisement in the *Guardian* for 4 February 1994;

URGENT PUBLIC SAFETY ANNOUNCEMENT
WORLD NEWS FLASH

From Astronomer Sofia Richmond

Halley's Comet is about to collide with the
planet Jupiter by mid-July 1994, causing the biggest
cosmic explosion in the history of mankind!!!

The broken fragments of the comet would then bombard
Earth, doing us no good at all. The remedy, she stated, was
in our own hands. For example, we must at once close
down all nuclear power stations and ground all aircraft; stay
in coal cellars or basements to avoid any heatwave; keep all
curtains drawn, and turn on all air-conditioning, and wear
dark glasses for safety all the time between 15 and 20 July.
Also, we must take care to put our affairs in order. It was
essential, for example, to destroy all pornography overnight,
replace beers and wines with non-alcoholic drinks, stop
all wars and fighting and reduce all crime in Saudi Arabia
by the use of capital and corporal punishment(!). Calling
herself Sister Maria Gabriel, she managed a good deal
of television publicity, and her appearance was certainly
unusual; her ash-blonde hair was tucked into a headscarf,
and she was attired in a long black cloak. Needless to say,
she wore dark glasses.

Her warning leaflets were sent to many people in
the public eye, including the Pope, the Chief Rabbi, the
British Prime Minister (then John Major), President Yeltsin,
the Polish Ambassador ('Sofia is a Polish astronomer, like
Copernicus'), the Queen, Prince Charles, King Hussain of
Jordan, Cliff Richard and, incidentally, me. Whether any of
the recipients took much notice is open to grave doubt, and
since then it seems that nothing more has been heard of her,
though no doubt she is simply biding her time.

Of the same genre is a Dr Robert Cremson, who has been described in the press as a famed astronomer and a NASA consultant, though, strangely, nobody in NASA has ever heard of him. In 1996 he announced that by studying photographs taken by the Hubble Space Telescope he had discovered a huge comet which was speeding Earthward 'like a runaway locomotive' and would probably hit us around 7 April. Clearly, then, action would have to be taken. Dr Cremson claimed that the authorities were very much on the alert, and that President Clinton of the United States had taken part in secret meetings with NASA and British scientists to work out the best way of destroying the comet before it could strike. He, too, now seems to have faded out of the public eye. It would be interesting to arrange a meeting between Dr Cremson and Sister Maria; they would have much in common!

With this brief excursion into what I can only call the Fruitcake Department, let us return to proper science.

It is true that we are not immune from bombardment. For example, in June 1908 a violent impact in Siberia blew pine-trees flat over a wide area, and had the missile hit a city, the death-toll would have been colossal. No crater was formed, and it is quite likely that the impactor was icy, which means that it was either a cometary fragment or else the nucleus of a very small comet which had crept up on us unseen. I will have more to say about this in the next chapter. In any case, there is absolutely no doubt about the cometary impact of July 1994 – not on Earth, fortunately for us, but on Jupiter.

Jupiter, the giant of the Solar System, is over 89,000 miles in diameter, and orbits the Sun at a mean distance of 483 million miles; its 'year' is nearly twelve times as long as ours. It has a very powerful pull of gravity – it is more massive than all the other planets put together – and it has a gaseous surface, overlying what we believe to be layers of liquid hydrogen, which in turn surround the hot, silicate core. It has a great influence upon the movements of comets, and many comets of short period have their aphelia (points of greatest distance from the Sun) at about the distance of the orbit of Jupiter, so that they make up what is called Jupiter's comet family.

On 22 March 1993 three American astronomers, Eugene and Carolyn Shoemaker and David Levy, took a photograph upon which they found the image of what Carolyn Shoemaker called 'a squashed comet'. It seemed to have been broken up into fragments, giving the impression of a string of beads, and it was in orbit not round the Sun, but round Jupiter. Calculations showed that it was doomed, and would inevitably crash into the giant planet during July of the following year. There could be no escape; the life expectancy of Comet Shoemaker-Levy 9 was indeed short. (The number indicates that this was the ninth cometary discovery by that particular team.)

It was found that the fragments – conveniently lettered from A to W – would rain down on the planet between 16 and 22 July, but nobody was sure quite what the results would be. There could be huge explosions, or there might be very little to be seen. On the night of the first impact, Fragment A, on 16 July, I was at Herstmonceux, formerly the site of the Royal Greenwich Observatory, using the powerful 26-inch refracting telescope. Fragment A hit Jupiter just beyond the limb, but the planet's quick spin soon brought the site into view, and the effects were amazing. A huge black spot appeared in the Jovian clouds, and as the other fragments landed the whole of Jupiter's southern hemisphere was transformed. On 19 July I recorded that the impact scars were 'the blackest things I have ever seen on Jupiter', and this was also the view of other observers. Photographs taken with the Hubble Space Telescope, and also by the Galileo spacecraft, which was then en route to Jupiter, confirmed that there had been huge fireballs, and that the temperatures had been staggeringly high.★

The effects of the impacts remained visible for months, though there were no permanent effects. But had Comet SL9 hit the Earth, the results would have been cataclysmic indeed. And this brings me on to Comet Swift–Tuttle, which has been described as 'the most dangerous object known to mankind'.

The comet was first seen in 1862; it was discovered independently by two American observers, Lewis Swift and Horace Tuttle. It was not brilliant, though it was visible with the naked eye and had a considerable tail. A few years later the celebrated Italian astronomer Giovanni Virginio Schiaparelli (best remembered today, perhaps, for his drawings of Mars, which he believed to be covered with a network of canals) made some valuable calculations showing that the comet was intimately linked with the Perseid meteor shower which is seen every August. Meteors are tiny particles, usually smaller than grains of sand, moving round the Sun; if a meteor happens to dash into the top of the Earth's resisting atmosphere it rubs against the air particles, and burns away, producing the effect known to us as a shooting star. Many meteors move around the Sun in shoals, so that every time the Earth plunges through a shoal we see a shower of shooting stars. The Perseids are the most reliable; normally the shower beings around 27 July and does not end until 17 August, with a maximum on 12 August. If you stare up into a dark, moonless sky for a few minutes at any time during the first fortnight of August, you will be very unlucky not to see at least a couple of shooting stars. The meteors seem to radiate from a position in the constellation of Perseus, which is why they have been so named.

★ The last word was said in a letter to *The Times*: 'How did astronomers know that Fragments A to W would hit Jupiter in strict alphabetical order?'

Schiaparelli calculated that the orbit of the Perseid shoal was practically the same as that of Comet Swift-Tuttle. This could not be due to coincidence, and it proved something which had long been suspected; meteors are simply cometary debris. Records of the Perseids go back to AD 36, and ever since about 830 they have been noted almost every year, though it was not until 1835 that their existence as a definite shower was recognized by two astronomers. A. Quetelet in Belgium and E.C. Herrick in the United States.

Mathematical work indicated that Comet Swift-Tuttle had an orbital period of 120 years, so that it would be back once more in 1982. However, 1982 came and went, and there was no sign of the comet. Many people (including me!) believed that we had simply missed it; after all, it had never been expected to be prominent. Then, however, Brian Marsden in America identified Swift-Tuttle with a comet seen much earlier, in 1737, by the Jesuit missionary Ignatius Kegler, observing from China. Marsden was able to refine the orbit, and found that the true period was 130 years, so that the next return was due in 1992. On 26 September of that year a Japanese amateur, Tsuruhiko Kiuchi, detected the comet as a dim object, below the eleventh magnitude, moving among the stars of Ursa Major. Obviously it was not going to come anywhere near us – as in 1862, when the minimum distance from Earth was 50 million miles – but Marsden found that there was some cause for alarm. The next encounter with Earth, according to the new orbit would be on 14 August 2126, and this time there would be a really close approach. In fact, there even seemed a chance of a direct hit.

We cannot be absolutely sure that this will not happen, but the latest calculations show that the odds are very much against it. On the other hand, Swift-Tuttle is fairly large by cometary standards – the nucleus may be around five miles across – and if it did crash down, it would cause immense devastation. No doubt there will be all sorts of alarms as 2126 approaches, and at least we may be sure that the comet will be a brilliant naked-eye object. I am only sorry that I will be unable to observe it myself – unless, of course, I live to the advanced age of two hundred and three.

Quite apart from actual impacts, can comets be dismissed as entirely harmless? According to two eminent astronomers, Professor Sir Fred Hoyle and Dr Chandra Wickramasinghe, the answer is 'no'. In 1978 they published a book in which they assumed that collisions with comets release viruses into our atmosphere, and that these viruses have unpleasant effects, producing epidemics ranging from influenza to smallpox. They even go so far as to claim that life originated well away from the Earth, and was brought here by a comet. Again we have a theory that represents a minority view, but which must not be dismissed out of hand. However, it does not involve the physical destruction of the Earth, and so does not concern us here. We must range further afield.

There has been one episode in recent times which was certainly not amusing. It was associated with a bright comet, Hale-Bopp. The comet appeared in 1996, and for much of 1997 was a very conspicuous object in the night sky. It was in fact the brightest comet in a long time, even though it did not rival some of the great comets of the past which actually cast shadows. I remember Hale Bopp very well indeed with its bright head and its lovely curved tail – or tails. One became very used to it and regretted its departure; it does go round the Sun, but will not return for several thousands of years.

Now for the problem in America (where else!). There was a religious group who called themselves Heaven's Gate led by a gentleman called Marshall Applewhite. Apparently its members believed that the Earth was about to be recycled (wiped clean) and their only hope of survival was to leave it immediately. According to them, Hale-Bopp was followed by a spacecraft which would obligingly pick up the followers of the cult and transport them to Heaven. Their method was to commit suicide and over thirty of them did. Well, that was their solution, but I rather doubt whether it turned out to be the correct one!

Cosmic Bullets

WORLD DISASTER MISSED BY THREE HOURS ... EARTH'S NARROW ESCAPE AS TINY PLANET PLUNGES BY. Such was a newspaper headline that greeted me one morning in late 1937. Other papers were hardly less sensational, and you might have been forgiven for supposing that the Earth was under a constant threat of cosmic bombardment.

In fact there really had been an encounter with a dwarf planet. The visitor was called Hermes (that was the name given to it by its discoverer, the German astronomer Karl Reinmuth), and it had scraped by at a mere 485,000 miles, which is less than twice the distance of the Moon. True, it was only about a mile in diameter, but its mass amounted to many millions of tons, and it would have caused havoc if it had landed upon a city. The newspaper headline was based on the revelation that if Hermes had crossed the Earth's orbit three hours earlier it might have scored a bull's eye upon the city then known as Leningrad (it has now, of course, reverted to his historic name of St Petersburg). Actually things are not really so simple as this, and neither St Petersburg nor any other city was in danger from Hermes at that particular moment, but the fly-by did a good deal to swing attention back to the possibility of asteroid collisions, and it was suggested that sooner or later we might be hit. Well, this possibility has again been rasied, and this brings me to the case of asteroid 2008 TC3.

It was discovered on 6 October 2008 by Richard Kowalski using the large telescope at Mount Lemmon north of Tucson. It was moving fairly quickly, and was obviously close. In fact, it very quickly became clear that it was going to collide with the Earth. The path indicated that the impact would occur in the Nubian desert in Sudan. The predictions were accurate and at 2.46 a.m. GMT on 7 October 2008 the asteroid entered the Earth's atmosphere at a height of about twenty-three miles above the desert it exploded. Fragments with a combined weight of 8.7lb were collected, and it seems that before its demise the object had been between seven and sixteen feet in diameter. The area is uninhabited, and in any case TC3 was too small to do much damage even if it had landed intact, but it does show that asteroid collisions can occur. If a large body hit us the results would be disastrous.

Yet what precisely is meant by an 'asteroid'? There are several classes of objects which could be potential sources of danger, and the distinction between them is not so clear as was believed only a few years ago, so let us examine the problem a little more closely. We must consider the following:

1   *Comets, already discussed.* The only part of a comet which is massive enough to do real damage is the nucleus. But when a comet has exhausted all its gas, it may assume the guise of –

2   *A small asteroid.* We do indeed have proof that this can happen. In November 1949 A.G.Wilson and R.G.Harrington discovered a faint comet, which had a short but unmistakable tail. It was not followed for long, but was thought to have a

short period of around 2.3 years. It was then lost – only to turn up again, thirty years later, in the guise of an asteroid; it has been given an asteroidal number, 4015. Of its identity there is no doubt at all. Two other comets, Neujmin 1 and Arend-Rigaux, seem also to have achieved this transformation during the past few decades, since they now look absolutely stellar; and another small asteroid, Phaethon, moves in almost the same orbit as the Geminid meteors, and is believed to be the 'parent' of that swarm. In fact, a small asteroid which may come close to the Earth may be nothing more than a dead comet, which has now lost all its volatiles. There are also –

3   *Meteorites, which are quite distinct from shooting-star meteors or cometary debris.* A meteorite is a solid body which comes from space and lands on the Earth; during its time spent in orbit round the Sun it should really be termed a meteoroid, but let us not confuse matters any more than is necessary. The real problem is to decide upon the dividing-lines between meteorites, asteroids and dead comets, and in this connection it may be appropriate to say something about any object that may possibly have belonged to any of the three classes. It came down at 7.17 pm, local time, on 30 June 1908 in the Tunguska region of Siberia.

Tunguska is not a thickly-populated area. It is in fact virtually uninhabited except for wandering tribesmen, which was fortunate on this occasion, because nobody was killed. (Incidentally, there is no reliable record of a fatality caused by a tumbling meteorite, though one or two people have had narrow escapes.) Shortly after 7.15 pm on 30 June, a brilliant object shot across the sky of Western China. It seems to have been brighter than the Sun, so that not even the most myopic observer could have overlooked it. Flashing over the Mongolian border, it descended quickly, and crashed down among the pine-forests of Siberia, blowing trees flat over a wide area and producing what was described as a pillar of fire visible hundreds of miles away. In the trading posts of Vanavara, forty miles at least from the impact point, the blast of heat was terrifying, and a few seconds later a shock wave ripped through the village, damaging many houses and breaking practically every window. One witness, S. Semenov, wrote: 'I was sitting on my porch facing north when suddenly, to the north-west there appeared a great flash of light. There was so much heat that my shirt was scorched on my back. I saw a huge fireball that covered a great part of the sky … Then it became dark, and at the same time I felt an explosion that threw me several feet from the porch.' Earthquake-recording stations in various countries observed shocks, and there were also meteorological disturbances. Almost 400 miles from the impact site, doors and windows in the station of Kansk, on the Trans-Siberian railway, rattled violently, while an approaching train was so badly jolted that the driver pulled up hastily to make sure that there had been no damage to the engine or track. Obviously, something very exceptional had happened.

Tunguska is one of the most desolate regions of Siberia. Partly because of this, and partly because of the internal disorders in Russia, no expeditions reached the site for a long time. The man who finally decided to tackle the mystery was a geologist, Leonid Kulik, who had studied at St Petersburg and had become a forester. He was interested in meteorites, and Tunguska fascinated him, but he had to bide his time. For a while the Bolsheviks imprisoned him as a suspected counter-revolutionary, which was true enough. Then came the First World War, and it was not until 1927 that Kulik managed to make his way to the scene of the explosion. When he did, he saw plenty of evidence of devastation. Not only were pine trees stilly lying flat, like matchsticks, but it was very clear that there had been a colossal blast of heat. What Kulik did not find was any evidence of meteoritic material, and he was equally unsuccessful on later expeditions; he never lost interest, and continued his studies up to the outbreak of the Second World War, which unfortunately he did not survive. In 1944 he was captured by the Germans, and died in a prison camp.

Neither has anyone else found meteorite fragments in the area, which opens up all sorts of possibilities. Weird theories were proposed, notably by a Russian science-fiction writer named Alexander Kazantsev, who maintained that the root cause was a nuclear blast. Flying saucer enthusiasts claimed that the missile was a visiting spaceship which made a forced landing and then blew up, while others suggested that the so-called meteorite might have been composed of 'anti-matter', so that when it came into contact with the Earth it was promptly annihilated.

A more logical explanation was offered by K. Florensky and other Soviet scientists. If the missle were the head of a small comet, the material would be icy; the tremendous frictional heat set up during the plunge downwards through the atmosphere would vaporise the ices, and on impact the whole missile would be destroyed, leaving no traces of meteoritic fragments or anything else. It has even been proposed that the object came from Encke's periodical comet. At any rate, the most recent major impact, which happened in 1947 in the general area of Vladivostock, was certainly due to a meteorite, because hundreds of fragments were collected. Again the region was uninhabited, and there were no casualties, but many small craters were produced.

Most museums have meteorite collections. You will see plenty, for instance, in the Geological Museum in South Kensington and in the National Maritime Museum at Greenwich, while if you happen to visit the Hayden Planetarium in New York you will see a true monster, weighing thirty-six tons, found by the explorer Peary in

1 The Leonid meteor shower of 1833, when it was said that meteors 'rained down like snowflakes' – regarded by William Miller as 'a sign of approaching doom'

2 The great comet of 1843, with its brilliant tail stretching across the sky, causing considerable alarm and despondency, particularly among the Millerites!

3 An astrological chart; it is by this sort of diagram that astrologers claim to be able to give reliable information about a person's character and destiny (!)

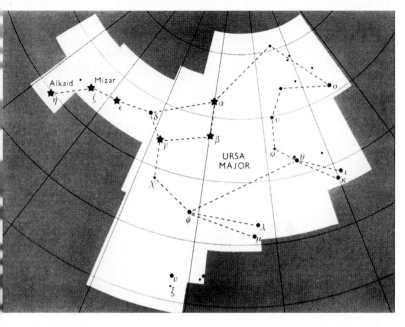

4 The Great Bear, with its seven famous stars making up the Plough or Dipper pattern; Mizar, with its small companion Alcor, is much closer to us than Alkaid.

5 Fishing – from an ark. Whether President Auriol actually landed any fish or whether his amazing ark was ever used for this innocent purpose is not recorded!

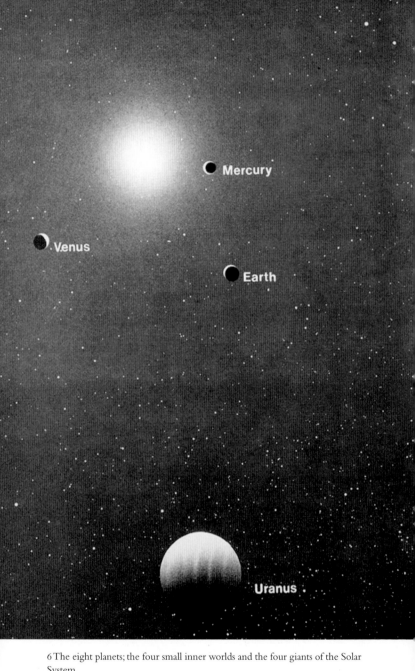

6 The eight planets; the four small inner worlds and the four giants of the Solar System.

Saturn

Jupiter

Neptune

7 The active Sun. Spots in plenty – and believed by Professor Porta to be due to the gravitational pulls of the planets upon the Sun's fiercely hot surface.

8 Relative positions of the planets for 1982, the year when, according to the *Jupiter Effect* writers, they should have been lined up.

9 Break-up of an ice moon, raining its fragments down upon the Earth with devastating results, according to Hörbiger and the disciples of WEL.

10 How the moon moves. It may hide the Sun and eclipse it; it may also pass into the Earth's shadow and be hidden for a while, or at least turned dim and coppery.

11 According to Bellamy, the approach of the moon will cause volcanoes on Earth to erupt violently.

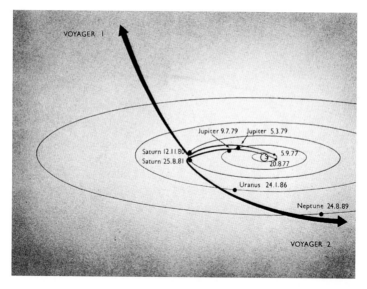

12 Interplanetary snooker. Voyager 1 bypasses Jupiter and Saturn before leaving the Solar System for good; Voyager 2 takes in Uranus and Neptune as well.

13 Monsieur Jacot's theory, in which the planets take part in what can only be described as a cosmic equivalent of musical chairs.

14 A menacing comet heads for Earth, its brilliant tail strung out behind it as it moves inwards, with the obvious intention of scoring a bull's-eye.

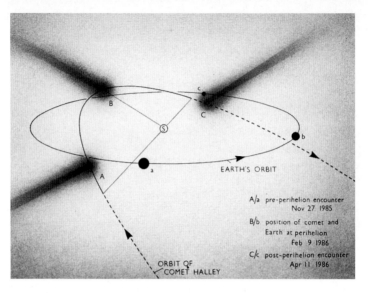

EARTH'S ORBIT

A/a pre-perihelion encounter
Nov 27 1985

B/b position of comet and
Earth at perihelion
Feb 9 1986

C/c post-perihelion encounter
Apr 11 1986

ORBIT OF
COMET HALLEY

15 Halley's comet in 1986; sadly it did not put on one of its best displays and was in no danger of being denounced by the Pope as an evil omen.

16 The great comet of 1811, noted for its brilliance and the straightness of its long tail.

17 Dr Velikovsky's theory: the Earth is shown to the lower left. Jupiter (upper right) has emitted the comet Venus (centre right), which has bypassed Mars (lower right) and has lost its tail, thereby being converted into a planet!

18 The Perseid meteors, radiating from a set area of the sky to produce an annual display of cosmic fireworks. Note the Demon Star, Algol, and the brilliant Capella.

19 An Earth-grazing asteroid with its grey, cratered surface. It may pass harmlessly by; it may hit us, causing devastation far greater than that of any nuclear bomb.

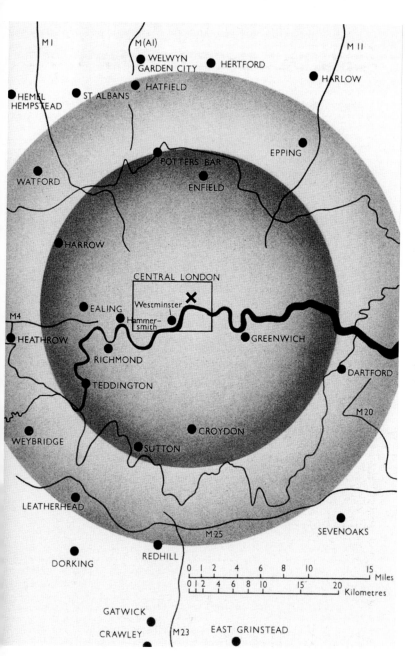

20 Effects of asteroidal impact on a city such as London. Areas out to and beyond
Hammersmith would be totally destroyed; the damage would extend out to St Albans and
Redhill.

21 Tunguska. The pine trees have stood silently and with dignity for many centuries –until the blazing visitor from outer space crashed down and laid them flat, scorching them in the process.

22 A puzzled dinosaur, looking up at a brilliant fireball streaking across the sky, and no doubt thinking that such things could never have happened in the Triassic Period!

23 Asteroids compared in size with Europe. Ceres, with a diameter of over 600 miles, is much the largest and most massive of the whole swarm, though Vesta is brighter.

24 The Sun's position in the Galaxy; (top) near the edge of a spiral arm, around 33,000 light years from the centre and (lower) lying almost in the main plane.

25 The sky from a planet near a globular cluster – a huge system of up to 1,000,000 stars, dominating one part of the sky and creating a brilliant light.

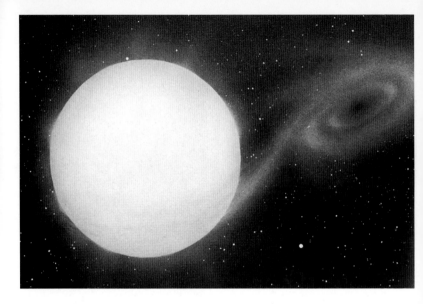

26 A Black Hole in orbit with a giant star. The Black Hole is pulling material away from the giant; before the material passes over the event horizon of the Black Hole, it is intensely heated and emits X-rays.

27 The Hertzsprung-Russell Diagram, of fundamental importance to all astronomers. The Main Sequence runs from upper left to lower right. The Sun is a typical Main Sequence star.

28 *The War of the Worlds* panic; Americans, still in their nightclothes, do their best to evade the 'Martians' described in the radio broadcast of H.G. Wells' novel.

29 The 'Big Bang'. Suddenly, and for reasons so far totally unknown, the universe comes into existence with a blaze which would make the most powerful supernova seem like a damp squib.

30 The Earth's fate is sealed; the Sun has begun to turn into a Red Giant, and the blaze of heat means that neither Earth not any other inner planets can survive.

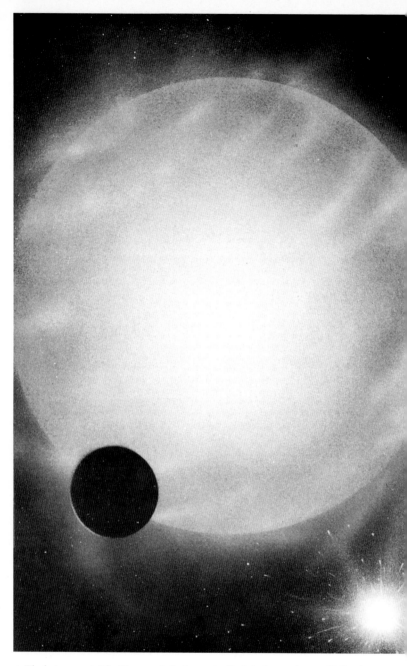

31 The last moments. The Moon explodes just as the Earth is about to be engulfed by the swelling Sun. Doomsday, as far as Earth is concerned, has come at last.

Greenland and laboriously transported to its present home. The holder of the heavyweight record is still lying where it fell in prehistoric times, near Grootfontein in South-West Africa; its estimated weight is at least sixty tons.

The most perfect example of a terrestrial meteorite crater is in Arizona, not so very far from the Lowell Observatory at Flagstaff. Its diameter is almost a mile, and it has become a noted tourist attraction. I recommend you to visit it if you are anywhere within range, though I warn you that if you scramble down towards the bottom you will find that climbing up the wall again, under a broiling Arizona sun, is decidedly exhausting.

There is absolutely no doubt that the Arizona crater is meteoric, and many fragments have been collected. Its age is believed to be about 50,000 years, so that the fall took place long before there were any local astronomers to observe it, and Red Indian legends about 'fire descending from heaven' are of relatively modern manufacture. According to well-informed estimates, the meteorite was about ninety feet in diameter, though the solid mass which finally impacted had been reduced by ten feet or so. The velocity as the meteorite landed was about 30,000 mph, and the explosion was equivalent to half a million tons of TNT, devastating the country over a range of at least a hundred miles. On impact, 90 per cent of the missile was vaporised; the remaining 10 per cent is buried under the southeastern rim of the crater. All animal and vegetable life in the danger-zone must have been instantly wiped out.

Other meteorite craters are known, a good example being that at Wolf Creek in Australia, but it is always wise to keep an open mind, as it seems that some alleged impact craters given in official lists are in fact volcanic – such as the Vredefort Ring in South Africa, some way from Pretoria. It is by no means so imposing as the Arizona crater, because the walls are low and are in places reduced to clumps of hills. Two villages – Parys, and Vredefort itself – lie on the crater floor, which is distinctive enough when seen from the air. Most geologists who have made exhaustive studies of it are convinced that it was formed by internal forces rather than by impact, because it fits in so neatly with the geology of the area, but opinions differ. At any rate, it is well worth visiting.

So far as solid worlds are concerned, cratering seems to be the rule rather than the exception. The Moon is an obvious example, and any small telescope will show hundreds upon hundreds of walled circular formations, ranging from tiny pits up to colossal enclosures more than 150 miles in diameter. Most astronomers now believe that these are impact structures, and that for a while in the early story of the Solar System there was a period of 'heavy bombardment'; Mars has many craters, and so have the main satellites of the outer planets. Mars has two tiny moons, Phobos and Deimos, and even these are crater-scarred; they are quite different from our own massive Moon, and are almost certainly ex-asteroids which wandered too close to the Red Planet and were unable to break free again. Neither would be of much use in lighting up the dark Martian nights.

This has been something of a digression. At least there is no doubt that if the Earth were hit by a major asteroid the results would be fatal, so let us dispose of these wordlets without further ado. In particular, are they themselves the remains of an old planet (or planets) which was broken up?

I must here say a little about Bode's Law, because it led to a systematic search for a new planet way back in the eighteenth century. It may or may not be a true Law; personally I doubt it, and neither should it be called after Johann Elert Bode, because it was originally worked out by a Wittenberg astronomer named Titius, and Bode merely popularised it. It came to general notice in 1772, and attracted a great deal of attention. Briefly, it is a mathematical relationship linking the distances of the various planets from the Sun, and it works like this:

Take the numbers 0, 3, 6, 12, 24, 48 and 96, each of which (apart from 3) is double its predecessor. Now add 4 to each. Taking the distance between the Earth and the Sun as 10 units, the other figures give the distances of the remaining planets from the Sun with fair accuracy. Hence:

Planet	Distance by Bode's Law	Real distance
Mercury	4	3.9
Venus	7	7.2
Earth	10	10 (because we made it so)
Mars	16	15.2
?	28	–
Jupiter	52	52.0
Saturn	100	95.4

Postponing any discussion of the question mark corresponding to Bode's 28, the agreement is not at all bad. Then, in 1781, William Herschel discovered the planet Uranus, which moves far beyond Saturn. The Bode distance for it should have been 196. Actually it was 191.8; again fairly good, and many people became confident that the Law was something more than sheer coincidence. However, the problem of No. 28 remained, and Bode suggested that there ought to be a planet there, even though a small one, moving round the Sun outside the orbit of Mars and inside that of the first of the giants, Jupiter.

The cudgels were taken up by six observers who called themselves the 'Celestial Police'. These were headed by Johann Schroter, who had a great reputation as an expert in all matters concerning the Solar System, and a Hungarian baron with the exotic name of Franz Xavier von Zach.

In 1800 they decided to divide up the sky into various sections, each 'policeman' being responsible for one section. Ironically, they were forestalled. At Palermo, in the island of Sicily, the Director of the Observatory, Piazzi, was busy making a new star catalogue when he happened upon a starlike object which moved against its background from night to night. Obviously it could not be a real star, and, sure enough, it proved to be the planet corresponding to Bode's number 28; the distance was found to be equivalent to 27.7. Piazzi christened it Ceres, after the patron goddess of Sicily.

The only trouble was that Ceres seemed to be disconcertingly small. We now know that its diameter is about 580 miles, and until recently it was thought to be even smaller than that. Even our Moon is over 2,000 miles across, and the Celestial Police regarded Ceres as frankly disappointing. Could there be any more worlds in the same region of the Solar System? They searched, and within the next decade they had identified three more, now called Pallas, Juno and Vesta. All were smaller than Ceres, and they became collectively known as minor planets, planetoids or asteroids. No others seemed to be forthcoming, and the Celestial Police disbanded – partly because Schroter's observatory at Lilienthal, near Bremen, was destroyed by the invading French soldiers in 1814, and the brass-tubed telescopes were looted because the soldiers believed them to be made of gold.

However, this was only the beginning. Asteroid No. 5, Astraea, was discovered in 1845 by a German postmaster-astronomer named Hencke, who had been searching tirelessly for over thirteen years. Others followed. Today, more than 2,000 have been observed sufficiently well to have their orbits worked out, and the entire swarm may contain at least 40,000 members, though most of them are very small, and Ceres is much the most massive member of the swarm – indeed, it contains more than half the mass of all the asteroids put together. Of the rest, only Pallas and Vesta are as much as 300 miles in diameter. Some of the asteroids are believed to be stony in composition, while others contain considerable quantities of iron. The mass of Psyche, the largest-known iron-type asteroid, is believed to be about 50,000 million tons, though we cannot hope to be at all precise.

If Bode's Law is truly valid, there seems little escape from the conclusion that a relatively large planet did once exist in the present-day asteroid zone, and was shattered in some way – and if this can happen to any planet of the Solar System, it could presumably happen to Earth as well. However, there are various weak points in the whole theory. In 1846 the planet Neptune was discovered as a result of some masterly calculations made by a French astronomer named Urbain Jean Joseph Le Verrier, later Director of the Paris Observatory, and according to repute one of the rudest men who has ever lived. (One of his colleagues commented that although Le Verrier might not be the most detestable man in France, he was certainly the most detested.) Le Verrier's calculations, and also those made independently by an Englishman, John Couch Adams, showed where the new planet might be; the key to the problem was provided by Uranus, which persistently wandered away from its expected path and was therefore presumably being tugged out of position by some unknown body. Neptune turned out to be a giant planet, slightly more massive than Uranus. Its distance on the Bode scale should have been 388, as you can easily show if you care to do a little arithmetic. Yet the true distance proved to be only 300.7, so that Bode's Law breaks down completely.

Once a Law fails in an important case, it is no longer a Law. Bode's comes into this class, and I have always tended to consider it in the same light as one of those 'take-away-the-number-you-first-thought-of' games. If so, then there is no longer any need to assume the former existence of a large planet between Mars and Jupiter, and most astronomers now believe that the asteroids were simply left over, so to speak, when the principal planets were formed. Certainly there is no chance whatsoever that the larger members of the swarm can leave the main zone, and so from them we are safe. We come, at last, to the maverick asteroids, which, as we have seen, may well be the nuclei of defunct comets.

The breakthrough was made in 1897 by Witt, of Berlin, who discovered an asteroid which had an exceptional path. It is No. 433 in the list, and Witt named it Eros. It is shaped rather like a sausage, with a longer diameter of eighteen miles, and it comes well within the orbit of Mars; at times, as in 1931 and 1975, it approaches the Earth to within a distance of roughly 16 million miles. This is still sixty times as remote as the Moon, but much closer than any of the main planets (Venus, not Mars as so many people think). It takes one and three quarter years to go round the Sun, and at its aphelion, or furthest point, it goes out beyond Mars.

The next major development came in 1932, when Karl Reinmuth, from Heidelberg, discovered an asteroid, 1862 Apollo, whose orbit actually crossed that of the Earth; its distance from the Sun ranges between 60 million and 137 million miles, so that its orbit can intersect that of Mars as well as that of the Earth. Two more 'Apollo' type asteroids were found in the 1930s, 2101 Adonis and, of course, Hermes – which was never given an official asteroid number, because it was not followed for long enough for a reliable path to be worked out, and it is, alas, 'lost' (we may locate it again one day, but the chances do not seem to be very good).

It began to look as though these bodies – never more than a few miles in diameter – were much commoner than had been expected, and this has indeed proved to be the case. Systematic searches for them were initiated in

1973, mainly by Eleanor Helin and Eugene Shoemaker, at Palomar Observatory in California. By 1989 a special 'Spacewatch' telescope had been set up at Kitt Peak, in Arizona, and another photographic search was begun from Australia in 1990. The hunt was on.

NEO (Near Earth Orbit) asteroids are now divided into three classes: Aten asteroids, whose mean distances from the Sun are less than that of the Earth, and whose orbital periods are less than a year. The first, 2062 Aten, was discovered by Eleanor Helin in 1976; its diameter is rather less than one mile, and all the other Atens are of the same kind. Apollo asteroids, whose orbits cross that of the Earth; their orbital periods are over a year. Amor asteroids, whose orbits cross that of Mars but not that of the Earth.

Much the largest of these is 1036 Ganymed, whose diameter is twenty-five miles. (Do not confuse it with Ganymede, the largest satellite of Jupiter; it is a pity that the names are so alike.) At perihelion Ganymed approaches the Sun to within 115 million miles, but fortunately for us it keeps well clear of the Earth. We are in danger only from the Atens and the Apollos.

Unquestionably there are swarms of these cosmic dwarfs, and so far we have located hundreds of them. One of the very smallest, still known by its catalogue designation of 1994 XM1, has a diameter of around thirty feet – approximately half the length of a cricket pitch. There is also asteroid 1991 VG1, where the diameter can be no more than twenty feet at most. Its nature is uncertain; there is a suggestion that it may be a piece of escaped artificial satellite debris rather than a bona fide asteroid!

I must also mention asteroid 1566 Icarus, discovered in June 1949 by Walter Baade. This is one of the very few asteroids known to approach the Sun to within the orbit of Mercury, so that near perihelion it is red-hot. At aphelion it moves out to 183 million miles, well into the main asteroid zone, so that it will be intensely cold. Icarus must have a most uncomfortable climate – a kind of cosmic Devil's Island. Despite its small size, it must weigh around 4,000 million tons, so that if it struck us it would do immense damage. Luckily, at the present epoch it cannot come closer than about 4 million miles, as it did in 1968 and again in 1987. But if we were hit by Icarus or an asteroid of comparable size, what then?

Remember, asteroids are solid enough to drop right through our atmosphere and land more or less intact. On impact, the kinetic energy of the asteroid's movement would be changed into heat, scorching everything over a wide area, and the missile might well penetrate the Earth's crust, thereby converting itself into a very effective bomb. Material would be hurled miles above the ground; if the crust were broken there would be devastating earthquakes, while if the asteroid plunged into the sea it would produce waves which would roar across the continents, washing away towns as rapidly as an incoming tide will demolish a sandcastle on the beach.

Various calculations have been made. For example, a 50-million-ton missile, landing at ten miles per second, would send a cloud of debris up to over twenty miles, spreading out over at least 150 miles in only sixty seconds. Icarus, which in size and mass is fairly typical of a maverick asteroid, weighs much more than that. So if the Earth were threatened in such a way, it is worthwhile to decide whether anything could be done about it.

During the 1968 Icarus approach, calculations were actually made by a group working at the Massachusetts Institute of Technology in the United States. They assumed that there would be several weeks' warning, so that there would be enough time – just! – to take action.

Various alternatives were proposed. It might be possible to land a nuclear missile on Icarus' surface and then explode it, thereby changing the orbit and diverting it from a collision course. Or the explosion might take place very close to Icarus, with the same result. Perhaps the asteroid might be attacked directly with a hydrogen bomb, either destroying it completely or else breaking it up into small pieces that would make no craters comparable with that which Icarus would produce if it landed intact – in which case the crater diameter would be of the order of fifteen miles.

This sounds straightforward, but there are many other factors to be taken into account. In particular, breaking up the asteroid – even if it could be done – would mean that we would be peppered with cosmic shrapnel. Diverting it by means of a nuclear explosion either on its surface or very close to it is a much better option, but to say that it would be difficult is a masterpiece of understatement. And in any case, can we be sure that the impactor would be detected in time? Many of the NEOs seen in recent years have been discovered only when they have made their closest approach to the Earth, and have started to recede.

To be honest, there is a near-certainty that a major collision will occur every now and then. Over geological ages the Earth cannot have escaped completely – I am not here referring to impactors which produce craters such as that in Arizona; I am considering asteroids large enough to cause global devastation. It is therefore worth casting around to see whether we can find any positive evidence, and this leads on at once to the problem of those most remarkable creatures, the dinosaurs.

As most people know, dinosaurs ruled the world for well over 100 million years. Some of them were harmless, while others, such as the Tyrannosaurus and Allosaurus, were anything but friendly; their huge bodies and their immense teeth would make them ferocious enemies, and while they held sway it was difficult for the smaller, less belligerent mammals to develop. Then, at the end of the Cretaceous

Period, the dinosaurs vanished, together with many other families of living things. Something unusual happened, and the puzzle of the death of the dinosaurs is one of the most fascinating in science.★

Theories abound. It has been suggested that at the end of the Cretaceous Period the Earth was bombarded by deadly short-wave radiations from an exploding star or supernova; alternatively, that the Sun cooled down for a few million years, so that the Earth's temperature dropped and the vast, unintelligent dinosaurs were unable to adapt; or that the climate was changed by violent volcanic activity. Another idea is that the dinosaurs simply came to the end of their evolutionary career, and 'died out'. Their departure seems to have been comparatively rapid, though whether their final decline lasted for less than a million years is still a matter for debate. Probably the most popular explanation at present is that of an asteroid impact, as originally suggested by Luis Alvarez in 1980. It has even been claimed that a large impact crater, Chicxulub off the Yucatan Peninsula, was formed by the impactor which put paid to the dinosaurs. The crater is around 110 miles across, and is buried under a deep layer of sediments, so that it is not easy to examine, but certainly it does seem to be of about the right age to account for the great extinction.

One strong supporter of the asteroid theory is Sir Fred Hoyle, who has even put forward an idea to limit the damage if another asteroid of comparable size hits us. His remedy may be unconventional, but it is certainly constructive.

Hoyle begins by working out the probable frequency of impacts by NEO-type asteroids. He comes to the conclusion that we may expect one hit every 250,000

★ I cannot resist mentioning a very small dinosaur, found in 1996 by a Chinese farmer. It seemed to be feathered, indicating a possible link with birds; the age was given as 120 million years old. Not unnaturally, it has been nicknamed Tweetieosaurus Rex!

years or so, but it is clear that the impact at the end of the Cretaceous was exceptional; it is worth bearing in mind that the largest-known Apollo asteroid, Hephaistos, is a full six miles in diameter. One effect of the impact, says Hoyle, was to hurl vast quantities of material high above the ground. These particles were reflective, so that for a period of at least ten years the Earth's upper air reflected back much of the radiation received from the Sun instead of allowing it to pass through to the ground. For a decade, then, the Sun's life-giving warmth was partly cut off. The oceans cooled dramatically; there were constant storms of freezing rain, and the light-level too was reduced. The dinosaurs, unable to see properly in the gloom, found that their food supplies were fatally depleted, and so they died out. The world had entered an Ice Age, and by the time conditions reverted to normal the dinosaurs were no more. Hoyle's calculations indicate that at least 50,000 million tons of debris must have been hurled into the upper atmosphere, so that the onset of the Ice Age was remarkably quick.

If this is valid, then another impact might cause a sudden Ice Age at any time. Hoyle's safeguard is to build vast pumps to stir up the waters of the oceans, bringing up the lower, very cold water to the surface and mixing it so as to prevent a sudden general cooling in the event of another Cretaceous-type strike. It would be necessary only to keep the oceans reasonably warm for a few years; this would be enough. Hoyle also maintains that such a project is well within our capabilities even at the present time, and, to quote his own words:

> The risk of an ice age is not just one of the biggest of the risks that we run. It is a risk that would hopelessly compromise our future. Besides wiping out a considerable fraction of those now alive, it would leave a wan, grey future from which the survivors and their descendants could do

nothing to escape. It would be a condition which might last 50,000 years or more, a future in which the prospects for mankind would be much less favourable than they are today. This is why our modern generation must take action to avoid catastrophe, an ultimate catatrastophe besides which the problems that concern people, media and governments today are quite trivial.

But would an impact of this kind trigger off an Ice Age, or would it have precisely the opposite effect? And, for that matter, can we possibly obtain proof that a major impact did occur 65 million years ago?

Some very significant results have been announced by Kenneth Hsu and his colleagues at the Swiss Federal Institute of Technology, who have given what they believed to be reliable confirmation of a Cretaceous strike, but reach results rather different from Hoyle's. They have been studying the sediments from the ocean floor off the coast of Southern Africa, and have found that between the layers laid down in the Cretaceous Period and its successor, the Eocene (by which time the dinosaurs had vanished), there are relatively high concentrations of the element iridium, which is known to exist in meteorites and presumably in asteroids as well. In this particular region there is also a relative lack of chalky material. Now, marine organisms use chalk (calcium carbonate) to build up their shells. Hsu believes that the impact caused a change in the composition of the surface waters; many families of organisms died, while the dust cloud sent up by the collision blotted out the Sun and stopped plant growth to a large extent. Plants remove carbon dioxide from the atmosphere, by the process of photosynthesis, replacing it with oxygen, so that when this process was halted the amount of carbon dioxide in the atmosphere increased. Since carbon dioxide acts in the manner of a greenhouse, shutting in the Sun's heat, the temperature rose, and the increased heat killed off the dinosaurs and many other living things as well. It took at least 50,000 years for conditions to become normal again, by which time the whole scenario of life on Earth had changed. Note that this idea involves an increase in temperature, not a Hoyle-type Ice Age, but here too a direct hit from an exceptionally large NEO asteroid is assumed to be the basic cause.

Efforts have been made to correlate earlier mass extinctions with asteroid impacts. Undoubtedly there were similar disasters during the Permian Period (230 million years ago), the Devonian (335 million years) and the Ordovician (435 million years). Moreover, it is possible that asteroid impacts may be linked with variations in the Earth's magnetic field.

The Earth acts as a huge magnet. At present the compass needle points to magnetic north (not the same as geographical north, but reasonably close to it), but there are indications that in the distant past the field was reversed, so that a compass needle would point south – as would be the case today on Jupiter, whose magnetic field is admittedly far stronger than ours. The origin of the Earth's magnetic field is to be found in movements in the liquid part of the iron-rich core. A sudden, violent impact could cause such global disturbance that the entire magnetic field might be disrupted, and it might even disappear completely for a while before the situation returned to normal. And if there have been times when the Earth had no magnetic field, the surface would have been left unprotected from various harmful radiations coming from space, with serious consequences for living organisms.

However, widespread damage is not the same as the total destruction of the world, and in a way I have been cheating in this chapter – I have been discussing not the end of the world itself, but the various ways in which it might be rendered uninhabitable. Asteroids, whether or not they are ex-comets, are not nearly massive enough to disrupt the Earth or even perturb its orbit to any measurable extent, while the main planets of the Solar System are in perfectly stable paths. Of course, there is always a chance that the Sun might happen to collect a wandering body large enough to shatter the Earth if it happened to score a bull's-eye, but the danger is so slight that we are entitled to ignore it. The Earth is around 4,600 million years old; it is roughly half-way through its life-story, and no such disaster has happened yet, even if a really major strike long ago was violent enough to result in the formation of the Moon. In the future we must expect impacts from NEO asteroids, but there is every reason to be confident that even in such a case we would be able to cope with the emergency much better than the dinosaurs did.

Star-Crash!

So far we have been discussing possible collisions with members of the Solar System; comets, asteroids or meteorites. But the Solar System is only a very small part of the Galaxy, and we must next turn to the awesome picture of an encounter with a wandering star.

If you take a pair of binoculars or a small telescope and look up at the Milky Way, you will see that it is made up entirely of stars. There are so many that to count them would be quite impossible, and to the unwary observer they seem so close together that they must surely be in imminent danger of bumping into each other. Outwardly, the Milky Way gives the impression of being a very crowded place indeed. Therefore, is our Sun in any danger of being hit by one of its stellar neighbours, with the inevitable destruction of the Earth?

The answer is almost certainly 'no', as astronomers realised as soon as they were able to draw up a reasonable picture of the Galaxy. The first man to do so on really scientific grounds was William Herschel, who came to England from his native Hanover when still a young man, and became a professional organist. In his spare time he made telescope mirrors and began to study the skies. He achieved fame in 1781, when he happened upon a new planet, the one we now call Uranus (you may recall that it fitted in neatly with Bode's Law), after which King George III gave him a modest pension, and Herschel became a full-time astronomer. He was undoubtedly one of the best and most enthusiastic observers of all time, though admittedly some of his ideas were odd. He even believed that there were intelligent beings living in a cool zone below the bright surface of the Sun.

Herschel set out to discover the shape of the Galaxy, and he decided to use the method of 'star-counts'. He could not hope to count every star visible in his telescopes, since this would have taken him a good many centuries; therefore he selected certain areas, and made 'star-counts' in them. Eventually he came to the conclusion that the Galaxy must be shaped like a 'cloven grindstone', which was not very wide of the mark even though he was wrong in assuming that the Sun, with the Earth, lay near the centre. We now know that the Galaxy is a flattened system with a central bulge, so that I have unromantically compared its shape to that of two fried eggs clapped together back to back. The yolks of the eggs correspond to the galactic nucleus, which we can never actually see because there is too much interstellar dust in the way. The Sun, plus its planets, lies well out from the nucleus towards the edge, not far from the main plane. The overall diameter of the Galaxy is of the order of 100,000 light-years; the Sun is slightly over 25,000 light-years from the centre of the Galaxy. (Remember that one light-year is equal to 5,880,000,000,000 or somewhat less than six million million miles.)

Seen 'from above' or 'from below', the Galaxy would show spiral arms, like a Catherine wheel. But from our vantage point the spiral structure is not evident. If we look along the main plane, we see many stars in roughly the same line of sight, i.e. almost one behind the other. This is the cause of the Milky Way band; the stars in it are not genuinely crowded together. There is no three-dimensional effect in space, and appearances can be highly deceptive.

Consequently, we cannot gaze at the Milky Way in the expectation of seeing two stars crash into each other and flare up in protest. Collisions must be very rare indeed, and it is very likely that a star such as the Sun can go right through its life cycle without experiencing even a near miss. We live in a fairly typical part of the Galaxy, just outside one of the spiral arms, and, as we have seen, the nearest star beyond the Sun is the dim red dwarf, Proxima Centauri, which belongs to the system of Alpha Centauri, one of the pointers to the Southern Cross and therefore too far south in the sky to be seen from Europe or most of the United States. Proxima is 4.2 light-years away, while Alpha Centauri itself is 0.1 of a light-year further out.

Now, 4.2 light-years corresponds to approximately 25 million million miles, and we are virtually certain that there are no stars closer than this; they would have been found by now. Alarms are sounded occasionally, and only a few years ago Olin J. Eggen, working at one of the major observatories in Australia, identified what he thought might be an even closer neighbour, but this turned out to be a mistake; Eggen's Star is a long way off, and Proxima remains the record-holder.

If there is no star within four light-years of us, then obviously there is no fear of a collision, at least in the foreseeable future. There are, of course, more densely-populated regions, particularly in the remarkable systems known as globular clusters, which are regular in outline and which are spectacular when viewed through an adequate telescope. The two finest examples, Omega Centauri and 47 Tucanae, are in the far south of the sky, but northern-hemisphere observers do at least have the great globular cluster in the constellation of Hercules, which is dimly visible with the naked eye as a misty patch if you know just where to look for it.

At the centre of a globular cluster, the average distance between individual stars is only about half a light-year, and any inhabitants of a plant moving round a star in such a region would have a glorious night sky; there would be many stars shining brilliantly enough to cast shadows, and there would be no proper darkness at all. Also, many of the stars would be red, because in the depths of a globular cluster the leading members are of the type known as Red Giants – a point to which I will return in Chapter 10. Against this, a globular-cluster astronomer would probably know very little about what lay beyond, so that his chances of studying the universe as a whole would be considerably less than ours.

Yet even inside a globular cluster, there can be few collisions. Space is very large, and relatively speaking the stars are very small. If you represent the Earth–Sun distance by one inch, the nearest star, Proxima, will be over four *miles* away.

It is relevant here to say a little about an old theory of how the Earth and other planets were born. According to the 'passing star' hypothesis, proposed at the turn of the century and popularised by Sir James Jeans (whom many people still remember both for his general books and for his radio broadcasts before and during the Second World War), a wandering star approached the Sun, and pulled off a cigar-shaped strip of material from the solar surface. As the visitor began to recede, the cigar was left whirling round the Sun; it broke up into drops, and each drop turned into a planet. One attractive feature of this scheme was that the largest planets, Jupiter and Saturn, lie where the thickest part of the 'cigar' would have been. When the mathematician attacked the theory it had to be somewhat modified, and it was even suggested that the passing star struck the Sun a glancing blow. Alas, even this would not do, and it has now been shown that the whole idea is out of court; like so many appealing and plausible theories, it simply does not work. According to modern ideas, the planets were formed from a 'solar nubula' or cloud of material associated with the youthful Sun.

I mention this because if Jeans had been right, then the Sun would have been one a very few stars to have met with a 'close encounter'. Planet families would have been excessively rare, and ours might have been the only one in the whole of the Galaxy. On the solar-nebula theory, planetary systems are likely to be commonplace, and this has been borne out by some indirect observations, since a few relatively close and lightweight stars seem to be 'wobbling' as though being pulled upon by invisible bodies of planetary mass.

It was a long time before we actually saw a planet of another star, but we now have definitive evidence. The bright star Fomalhaut is the southernmost of the really bright stars to be visible from Britian, or anywhere in Europe. It is over twenty light years away and considerably more powerful than our own Sun. It had long been regarded as a suitable candidate as a centre of a planetary system, and our best telescopes have now managed to image the planet as a tiny dot. It is much more like Jupiter than like the Earth, and we certainly could not live there, but its very existence indicates that planets are likely to be very common in our galaxy.

The Galaxy is rotating, and the Sun takes about 225 million years to complete one journey round the centre. This is sometimes termed the 'cosmic year'. One cosmic year ago, the Earth was in a primitive state; the most advanced life-forms were amphibians, the ancestors of today's frogs and toads, while even the dinosaurs had yet to make their entry. Other stars share in the rotation, but there are some which travel in different paths, and I suppose that we cannot entirely rule out the chance of a collision at some time or other. It is excessively improbable, but it is not impossible. What we can say, with confidence, is that it will not happen yet.

We would have plenty of warning. The first indication would be the movement of one particular star in the sky relative to its background, showing that it must be unusually close. Over the years, or over the centuries, it would brighten up very gradually, until it became prominent enough to be visible with the naked eye. No doubt every Government would do its best to hide the truth because of a fear of mass panic, but eventually it would leak out, and you can well imagine the frantic preparations, though it is not easy to see what could be done without mass emigration to another world – and which world? The whole of the Solar System would be disrupted. Decades more, and the unwelcome newcomer would start to dominate the night sky; then, comparatively quickly, it would become visible in the day-time as well, shining down menacingly as it swooped inwards. At last it would cross the orbits of the outermost planets, and would sear and destroy any which were unfortunate enough to be in the danger-zone. Coming closer and closer, it would perturb the orbit of the Earth; now there would be two suns instead of one, and the whole climate would alter, both because of the extra heat and because of the orbital change. Huge tidal waves would sweep across the continents; if the temperature were raised sufficiently the atmosphere would be driven off, and violent earthquakes would begin, so that the world would revert to its Pre-Cambrian state, when it had still not cooled down sufficiently for life to appear. A direct collision between the Sun and the star would cause an outburst so tremendous that all the inner planets, at least, would be vaporised. Even if there were no actual contact, the star would recede once more leaving behind it a wounded Sun and the ruined remnants of a planet family.

However, it does not seem likely that the Sun will encounter a wandering star during the 5,000 or 6,000 million years left to it before it changes its structure dramatically enough to destroy the Earth without any outside help. There is no stellar candidate on view at the moment, so that at the very worst we have many thousands of years' grace!

There is one other possibility. I have been talking about normal stars, shining in much the same way as the Sun, but stars do not last forever, and eventually they die. The Sun itself will pass through various stages of senility, but it seems certain to end up as a dead, dark globe – in fact, a black dwarf. Other stars will meet with a similar fate. Whether the universe has existed for long enough to allow many stars to reach the black dwarf condition is questionable, but there ought to be some, and of course they would be extremely hard to detect, because they would send out no radiation at all. We must consider the chances of a meeting with a dead star of this kind.

There is no positive proof that our part of the Galaxy is lacking in black dwarfs, and there is even a recent theory that suggests that there may be one in the Solar System itself. The idea is highly speculative, but it is certainly worth looking at rather more closely, which means delving back into history. All the planets out as far as Saturn were known in ancient times, and they could hardly have been overlooked, because they are prominent naked-eye objects (even Mercury can be quite conspicuous when best placed). As we have seen, Uranus was discovered by Herschel in 1781. He was not looking for a new planet, and did not even recognise it when he found it; he mistook it for a comet, but it would be rather unfair to dismiss his discovery as sheer chance. He was carrying out a systematic review of the sky, and, as he said, if he had missed Uranus on one night he 'must have found it the next'.

Irregularities in the movements of Uranus led to the tracking down of Neptune. Much later, Percival Lowell, the American astronomer who is best remembered today for his admittedly wild theories about intelligent Martians, made calculations of the same sort. He believed in a ninth planet, and in 1930, Clyde Tombaugh, at Lowell's observatory, discovered Pluto not far from the calculated position.

The irregularities of the movements of Uranus and Neptune are of little help, because they are so slight, but now there is a new way of approaching the problem. We may be able to make use of artificial rocket probes, and there are two such spacecraft, Pioneers 10 and 11, which seem to be ideal for the purpose. I modestly claim to have suggested something of the kind in a paper published as long ago as 1975, though in a much less precise form.

Pioneers 10 and 11 were designed to make close-range studies of Jupiter. It was impossible to bring them back to Earth; they would be travelling so fast that they would escape from the Solar System altogether, and would presumably wander around in interstellar space until they were destroyed by collision with some solid body. Each carried a radio transmitter which would be adequate to maintain contact well after the main part of the mission was over. (They were also fitted with plaques, just in case they were picked up by some alien civilisation – the idea being that the plaques would give a firm clue as to their planet of origin.) Pioneer 10 was launched in 1972, and in December 1973 it passed within striking distance of Jupiter, sending back the first really reliable information about that strange and decidedly hostile world. After its encounter it continued to move outward, and by now it is a long way beyond the orbits of Neptune and Pluto.

Pioneer 11 followed a year later. It encountered Jupiter in December 1974, but its work was not over. It still had some fuel reserve, and so it was given an extra burst of power which swung it back across the Solar System to an encounter with Saturn in 1979, after which it too embarked on its never-ending journey. Note that the two Pioneers are leaving the Solar System in opposite directions, and we are still in contact with them. Suppose, then, that they start to wander away from their predicted paths? We could use them in much the same way that Lowell used Uranus and Neptune, and under favourable circumstances they might even lead us on to a new member of the Sun's family. But there are other intriguing possibilities, too.

The whole situation has been complicated by the discovery that Pluto is not a proper planet at all. Other bodies of the same kind have been discovered in the remote parts of the Solar System, and at least one of these, Eris, is larger than Pluto. Many hundreds of these objects have been found, making up what we call the Kuiper Belt. The new discoveries make it much less likely that another major planet does exist out there, and to be candid I am rather sorry about this − I was so sure that it would be found one day!

First, take the case in which one Pioneer wanders off course, but not the other. This would indicate a gravitational pull from an outer planet which could not make itself felt on the opposite side of the Solar System. As I said in my original paper, it would be the longest of long shots, because Planet Ten would have to be in just the right place at just the right time, but it could happen.

Next, suppose both probes started to wander. The chances of there being two suitably-placed outer planets would be negligible, and a more plausible candidate would be a much more massive body at a greater distance – say 50,000 million miles or so. Compared with a distance of this sort, the diameter of the Solar System is small, and the Pioneers could be regarded as being at equal distances from the perturbing body, just as for all practical purposes it is good enough to say that Westminster Bridge and the Houses of Parliament are the same distance from the Statue of Liberty.

The same principles apply to the Voyagers, which were sent on their way in 1977. Voyager 1 encountered Jupiter in 1979 and Saturn in 1980 before starting on its final outward journey. Taking advantage of the alignment of the giant planets at that period, Voyager 2, as we have seen, carried out a more ambitious programme: Jupiter (1979), Saturn (1981), Uranus (1986) and Neptune (1989). The Voyager transmitters are more powerful than those of the Pioneers, and we may hope to maintain contact until they reach the edge of what is termed the heliosphere – that is to say, the distance at which the solar wind ceases to be detectable. There is also the question of the Oort Cloud, which is believed to be made up of a swarm of icy bodies – comets, in fact – orbiting the Sun at a distance of at least one light-year. None of the probes will stay in touch until they reach this Cloud, but there is another aspect to be born in mind. Some astronomers believe that the Sun has a massive companion moving in a very elliptical orbit. Occasionally this body invades the Oort Cloud, and icy bodies are torn out of the Cloud itself and sent hurtling Sunward – to appear in our skies as comets.

What could this body be? A massive planet? More probably a Brown Dwarf star, or even a dead Black Dwarf; but we are wandering into the realm of pure speculation. All we can say is that if there is such a body, 'Nemesis', there is always a very slim chance that it could swing inward. It would be very unlikely to collide with us, but its pull could easily result in throwing our luckless world into a new orbit and making it uninhabitable. The Earth would survive, but humanity would not.

An even more exotic idea is that the perturbing body might be a Black Hole, at a still greater distance – possibly as much as a couple of light-years. A Black Hole is the remnant of a very highly-evolved, very massive star which has collapsed, and is now pulling so strongly that not even light can escape from it; the stellar remnant has surrounded itself with a sort of 'forbidden zone' which is to all intents and purposes cut off from the rest of the universe. The tremendously strong gravitation pull can suck in material from outside, and it has been said that a Black Hole is a cosmic cannibal, gobbling up material and removing it from all contact with the rest of space. The Sun is not nearly massive enough to create a Black Hole, (see Chapter 10), and so if the hypothetical companion is of this type it must have been produced by a star much more massive than the Sun, which does not seem very likely. In any case, any Black Hole solar companion would be so far away that we are well beyond its danger zone. On the other hand, we cannot entirely rule out the chance that there are wandering, undetectable Black Holes in the Galaxy, and there must be a slight but non-zero possibility of trouble on that score.

Can there be any danger from a more 'normal' star? Most stars are stable, and shine unchanged for immense spans of time, but there are some which are highly explosive. Into this category come the novae and, above all, the supernovae. Nova means 'new', but a nova is not genuinely a new star at all. What happens is that a formerly very faint star flares up suddenly, becoming hundreds of thousands of times its normal brilliance and remaining prominent for a few weeks or months before fading back to obscurity. Novae have been seen often enough, and some of them have become spectacular. The nova seen in the constellation of Aquila (the Eagle) in 1918 briefly outshone all the stars in the sky apart from Sirius. The last bright nova flared up in 1975 in Cygnus (the Swan), and became brighter than the Pole Star, though its glory was short-lived, and after a week or so it had become too dim to be seen with the naked eye.

Novae were once believed to be due to head-on collisions between two stars, but this cannot be correct; as we have seen, stellar encounters are very rare indeed, and novae are much too frequent to be collision products. In any case, we have now been able to find out a great deal about them. It seems that a nova is really a two-star or binary system, and that one member of the pair drags material away from the other; eventually the system becomes so unstable that a flare-up results. There are also a few stars which have been known to undergo more than one nova-like outburst, notably the 'Blaze Star', known officially as T Coronae, which bursts forth in 1866 and again in 1946.

A supernova is quite different, and what we call a Type II supernova is due to the sudden collapse and subsequent destruction of a very massive star. At its peak a supernova outburst may emit at least a thousand million times as much energy as the Sun, plus a flood of lethal radiation which would do the Earth no good at all if we happened to be anywhere near.

Supernovae are uncommon. In our Galaxy, the only supernovae to have been seen during the last thousand years have been the stars of 1006, 1054, 1572 and 1604 – all in pretelescopic times. However, they are so luminous that they can be detected in remote galaxies millions of light-years away, and many have been observed in recent years. Quite a number have been discovered by amateur astronomers, who know the night sky a great deal better than the average professional.

From the vague accounts which have come down to us, the 1006 star, in the southern constellation of Lupus (the Wolf) became almost as bright as the quarter-Moons; we know where it was, because we can still detect long-wave-length radio emissions from its site even though the star itself has long since vanished. The 1054 supernova, described by Chinese and Japanese astronomers, flared up in Taurus (the Bull), and has left the patch of expanding gas which we call the Crab Nebula, much too faint to be seen with the naked eye or most binoculars, but magnificent when photographed through a powerful telescope. Since then we have had the supernovae of 1572, in Cassiopeia, and 1604, in the Serpent-bearer. All these old supernovae are radio sources, and it is fortunate for us that they were so far away. The distance of the Crab Nebula is about 6,000 light-years.

There has been one recent naked-eye supernova – in 1987, not in our Galaxy, but in an outer system, the Large Cloud of Magellan. Even at its distance of 169,000 light-years, the supernova became as bright as the Pole Star. Unfortunately it was too far south to be visible from Britain, and it has long since faded so much that it has become invisible except through a powerful telescope.

Unquestionably a nearby supernova would threaten all life on Earth, but only very massive stars can explode as supernovae, and there are no stars of this type within range. For supernova candidates we must look for Red Giant stars, which are well advanced in their life histories. (True, the 1987 progenitor star was a blue giant, but this particular supernova was atypical in many ways.) One of the nearest Red Giants is Betelgeux, in Orion, which according to the authoritative Cambridge catalogue is 310 light-years away. Its diameter is of the order of 200 million miles, large enough to contain the entire orbit of the Earth round the Sun; it is unstable, and slightly variable in light. It could match 15,000 Suns, so that it is a true cosmic searchlight even now. If it 'went supernova' it would indeed be glorious, but this may not happen for a very long time yet.

Actually, the best potential supernova candidate is Eta Carinae, in the far south of the sky. For a time during the last century it outshone every star in the sky except Sirius; at its peak it seems to have had about 6 million times the luminosity of the Sun. It is exceptionally massive, and is associated with a magnificent nebula, or cloud of dust and gas. For a century now it has been invisible with the naked eye, but it is still very powerful, and may indeed have lost none of its total luminosity, because a good deal of its light may be blotted out by interstellar material. There are strong indications that Eta Carinae is approaching its crisis, and that it may be getting ready to destroy itself in a supernova explosion; certainly it cannot continue shining in its present form for more than a million years or so, which is not long on the astronomical timescale. However, it too is so remote that it could do no more than provide a superb and fascinating spectacle.

There have been suggestions that the Earth was bombarded by deadly radiation sent out by what is called a 'gamma-ray' burster. We now that there are strange objects called black holes, which have been identified even though we cannot see them. (I will have more to say about them later.) A black hole is produced when a very massive star collapses, and ends up by pulling so strongly that not even light can escape from it. The old, dying star is surrounded by a sort of 'forbidden zone' which is cut off from the rest of the Universe. The idea proposed is that when two black holes collide they merge to form a single black hole, sending out an absolutely incredible amount of radiation before settling down. The radiation is mainly in the form of gamma rays, and if the Earth were anywhere within thousands of light years of the explosion it would do no good at all. Luckily, it does not seem that there are any black hole candidates within range of the Earth at the moment, so we need not have much fear on that score.

Finally, in our list of possible cosmic disasters, we come to the material spread between the stars. There is much more of this than used to be thought, and it has been suggested that the periodical Ice Ages have been caused when the Sun enters a 'dusty' region, perhaps in one of the spiral arms of the Galaxy, and has its supply of solar radiation drastically reduced. There have been many science-fiction novels written on this theme, notably Sir Fred Hoyle's *The Black Cloud*, but it does not seem to be a serious threat. Moreover, the Sun left the last spiral arm at least 10,000 years ago, and we are not due to enter another in the foreseeable future, though it is fair to say that our knowledge of how spiral arms are formed is still very incomplete.

All in all, it seems that we are in no danger from supernovae or interstellar clouds. Neither is there much chance of an encounter between the Sun and another star, and at the very worst nothing of the kind can happen for millions of years. Much more probably it will never happen at all, so that there is little chance of the Earth being wiped out by a maverick sun.

Ordeal by Flying Saucer

I have never personally been involved in an end-of-the-world scare.* Discounting the mild alarm caused by John Gribbin's Jupiter Effect, none has occurred in England since I was born, and I doubt whether there will be any in the near future. But I have met several people who have vivid memories of a celebrated American scare which occurred on 31 October 1938, and is in a class of its own.

The whole episode was quite unintentional. The man unwittingly behind it was no less than Orson Welles, then a rising young film and radio director. From New York, he decided to put on a wireless adaptation of *The War of the Words* by his near-namesake, H.G. Wells, which had been published

---

* I must, however, admit that on one occasion I was responsible for a hoax. On 1 April I went on the air, in one of the BBC breakfast programmes, and announced that at 10 am Pluto would pass behind Jupiter; this would cause a reduction in gravity, and everyone would feel a loss of weight. The only way to detect this, I said, was to jump up and down and see how high you would go. I was unprepared for the outcome. The BBC lines were jammed, and many people – including some courting couples – rang to say that they had indeed found the effect very marked … I was, however, upstaged on a later 1 April by my old friend Professor Samuel Tolansky, FRS, who fried onions in front of the television camera and broadcast smells. The number of people who smelled those onions was truly astounding!

long before and had been accepted as a science-fiction classic. To those of you who have not read it, the plot is centred upon an invasion of the Earth by grotesque monsters from Mars, who land in Horsell Common, near Woking in Surrey, and run amok with their fighting machines, heat-rays and other charming devices calculated to do the denizens of Earth no good at all. Resistance is futile, and all seems lost, but Nature comes to the rescue at the eleventh hour; the Martians are destroyed by terrestrial bacteria, which are absent on their own planet, and against which they have no protection.

Remember that at that period the idea of intelligent life on Mars had not been definitely ruled out. When *The War of the Worlds* was written, in 1901, Percival Lowell and his followers were giving convincing descriptions of Martian canals, which, it was said, had been built by the local residents to form a planet-wide irrigation system on a world desperately short of water. All the ice and snow locked up in the white polar caps was pumped through to the warmer regions, which were centres of population, and the blobs or 'oases' where two or more canals intersected were regarded as the equivalent of cities. Lowell did not believe in hostile aliens, and indeed he took care to point out that on a planet such as Mars the inhabitants would have to work together; war, he added, was a childish pastime, and the Martians had presumably progressed far beyond any such thing. But of the habitability of Mars he had no doubt at all, and he went so far as to write: 'That Mars is inhabited by beings of some sort or other is as certain as it is uncertain what those beings may be.'

By 1938 many doubts had been expressed, but there was no final proof that the Martians did not exist; it was not until the Space Age, with the flights of the Mariner and Viking probes, that we found out what Mars is really like – a mountainous, cratered world, with lofty volcanoes and dry riverbeds but, unfortunately, no canals. And this lay decades ahead when Orson Welles planned his broadcast.

In his adaptation of the novel, Welles transferred the scene of action from Woking to the United States, and began by putting out what many listeners took to be an actual news bulletin. The effects were startling. I quote here from the London *Daily Mirror* of the following day, I November 1938:

Millions of Americans are today still suffering from nervous prostration after the panic that swept across the country last night during the broadcast of *The End of the World*, a radio adaptation of H.G.Wells' *War of the Worlds*.

Doctors and chemists are reaping a harvest of dollars; hospitals and doctors' surgeries are thronged with nervous breakdown cases. The sales of nerve tonics have soared upwards.

From all parts of the country come reports of people having arms and legs broken in stampedes during the panic. Millions of American listeners mistook the Wells fantasy for news, and the war scare spread as the radio told of an invasion from Mars.

Thousands got the news second-hand, and soon reports spread that German troops in powerful 'planes and Zeppelins were landing on US soil.

All over America thousands of listeners ran from their homes into the streets, wrapping damp towels round their heads, screaming for gas-masks, falling on their knees in prayer, or dashing off to the countryside, fainting and screaming.

Today there is an impressive reaction, with doctors and nurses rushing to new cases.

Lawyers also report a great increase in business from listeners who plan to sue the radio company and everyone responsible for the broadcast, although during the broadcast commentators did several times try to make it clear that it was fiction.

Psychologists of Columbia and other universities, exalting last night's madness as the greatest mass panic in world history, are calling on listeners for data.

Many people treated by doctors today were still crying hysterically.

One woman patient in a down-town hospital insisted, 'I know it's true. Hundreds are dead somewhere. Roosevelt himself announced it over the radio. I recognised his voice.'

Some insist they saw planes and robot soldiers land from tubular metal ships and fire death-ray guns. Panic lingered longest in Harlem, New York's Negro section, where hundreds prayed nearly all night in the streets. Hundreds fought their way into Father Divine's famous temple 'to see the end of the world come'.

Others barricaded themselves in their homes, even blocking windows with furniture 'to keep out the men from Mars'.

At Concorde, Washington, just as the broadcast was announcing that 'monsters were flocking down on United States soil', the lights went out in most of the homes due to a failure in the power.

Terrified inhabitants thought the invasion had reached Washington State, and the town for a time verged on mass hysteria. Women fainted, and men prepared to take their families to the mountains…

From the few eye-witness reports that I have had, I feel that the *Mirror* writer may have exaggerated things somewhat, but of the panic itself there was no question. People actually saw fighting machines, felt the heat-rays and witnessed luckless folk being fried like eggs in the searing blasts. And here, surely, we have a forerunner of the flying saucer or UFO stories that are still with us.

Mars has always been regarded as the planet most likely to harbour intelligent life, and there have been various efforts to establish contact. I particularly like the idea put forward in the 1870s by a Frenchman called Charles Cros, who wanted to build a huge burning-glass and focus the Sun's rays on to the Martian deserts, swinging the lens around and writing words. I have often wondered what words he meant to write – and what would have been our own reactions if the Martians had responded similarly, so that vast letters had started to appear in the Sahara? There was always the possibility that the Martians would be civilised enough to speak English or some other terrestrial language, but the whole method seemed somewhat cumbersome, and the French Government refused to finance it, so that it was never actually put to the test. At the turn of the last century a prize was offered, again in France, to anyone who could get in touch with an extra terrestrial civilization, but Mars was specifically excluded, because the donors thought that calling up the Martians would be too easy.

Various wireless messages have been sent, and in 1924 the British Post Office went so far as to accept a telegram for a Martian address, charging 1s 6d. per word but prudently marking it 'Reply not guaranteed'. And in 1939, a year after the Welles scare and at a time when Mars was particularly brilliant, a Surrey radio amateur who rejoiced in the name of A. Bird claimed that he had succeeded in receiving coded signals from the Red Planet, though to the best of my knowledge he never revealed what the Martians had said.

Today we know much more about Mars than we did in the days of Lowell, or even Mr Bird. Spacecraft have been past and have actually landed there. The great breakthrough came in the 1960s, with the Soviet and American probes. The Russians were the first to make the attempt, although their rocket Mars 1, launched in 1962, probably did go within a couple of hundred thousands miles of its target it had lost contact by that time, and the first success came in 1964 with the American Mariner 4. This was a camera-carrying probe which sent back close range pictures of the Martian surface, showing a world which was not in the least like anything we had expected. There were mountains, craters, and valleys – in fact it seemed much more like the Earth than like the Moon. Our probes followed, both Russian and American. In 1976 two American Viking spacecraft made gentle landings, and sent back pictures direct from the surface. The scene was one of reddish, barren rocks under a yellowish-pink sky, and the air turned out to be far more tenuous than anyone had predicted; in fact it is quite useless so far as our kind of life is concerned. Moreover it is made up not of oxygen and nitrogen, but of carbon dioxide and we cannot breathe that.

There followed even more striking developments. The Pathfinder probe of 1996 landed in the area of Mars called Ares Vallis and took a small vehicle with it, Sojourner, which moved around and continued to send back data for some months. Then, in 2003, came the launch of two probes which really have revolutionised the whole picture; these were the American vehicles Spirit and Opportunity, which not only landed safely but moved around under their own power and were still working quite happily in 2009. So what is the picture we have of Mars now?

Well, not particularly inviting. There are huge volcanoes almost certainly completely extinct, there are vast craters and there are deep valleys. The dark areas once thought to be oceans are simply regions where the red, dusty stuff has been blown away by winds in the thin Martian atmosphere, exposing the darker materials beneath. Yet analysis of the material shows that Mars was once a world with extensive seas, a denser atmosphere, and a general environment that would have suited life.

What we do not know is whether life actually appeared there, the chances seem to be fairly good; however, it seems reasonable to assume that life never managed to get very far before the atmosphere leaked away because of the weak gravitational pull, and Mars became far less welcoming. There may be life on Mars, but primitive and single-celled – we cannot expect anything as advanced as a beetle, or even a blade of grass. Before long, we should be able to find out, because there is every hope of sending a sample and return mission to bring us back a piece of Mars which we can study in our laboratories. As for the chances of Martian life today — I have to admit that I think the chances are around 50/50. Intelligent life, on the other hand, can be discounted. Lowell's brilliant Martian engineers belong to science fiction, not science fact.

We have to admit that Mars is less hostile than any other world in the Solar System, and the rest seem to be fairly hopeless. Mercury has practically no atmosphere and a climate that is vigorous by any standards. Venus is scorching hot, with a surface temperature of hundreds of degrees and a crushing atmospheric pressure; the atmosphere itself is almost pure carbon dioxide. The outer giant planets are not solid except at their cores; Jupiter and Saturn are gas giants, arid Uranus and Neptune are ice giants, though most of the ices are in liquid form.

At least the giants have moons of their own, and these are decidedly interesting. Jupiter has four big satellites, and of these one of them – Io is wildly volcanic, while another, Europa, has an icy surface underneath which there is probably an ocean of ordinary water. Could anything survive in a sunless sea of that kind? I very much doubt it. In Saturn's family of moons there are two which are of special note. Titan is larger than our Moon, and actually larger than the planet Mercury, and it does have a substantial atmosphere made up chiefly of nitrogen, but it is bitterly cold, and most unfriendly. We know a great deal about it because one spacecraft, Huygens has actually made a controlled landing there and sent back pictures direct from the surface.

There are lakes, made up not of water but of chemicals such as methane and ethane, so that you cannot conjure up any picture of fishing trips in Titan's Lake District. The other interesting satellite Enceladus is a mere three hundred miles in diameter, but there are geysers of ice spouting out from one of its poles, so that presumably there is an ocean underneath. This defies all explanation; the fountains of Enceladus simply ought not to be there; so far as life in the Solar System is concerned I think we have drawn a halt. Pluto and the other members of the outer belt are unsuited in every way.

Yet … what about flying saucers? Do they exist, and if so, do they pose any threat either to mankind or to the Earth itself?

The saucer story began abruptly on 24 June 1947. A businessman named Kenneth Arnold was flying his private aeroplane over the Cascade Mountains, in Washington State, when he saw nine circular objects in obvious formation, moving at a high speed and passing him at a distance which he estimated as twenty-five miles (though I am not clear as to how he arrived at this figure). He wrote: 'They flew like a saucer would if you skipped it across the water' – and the term 'flying saucer' was born.

Arnold believed that he had seen space-ships from another planet; he also believed that officialdom was dedicated to playing down his story and suppressing the great truth – here, of course, we have the Conspiracy Theory syndrome. Before long other reports, even more sensational, started to come in thick and fast, but the real crunch came in 1953, with the publication of the classic book *Flying Saucers Have Landed*, written jointly by George

Adamski and Desmond Leslie, both of whom I knew though both have now died. The really intriguing part of the book was Adamski's account of his first meeting with an alien from Venus, which, he said, took place at 12.30 pm on 20 November, 1952.

It occurred, according to Adamski, near Parker in Arizona, actually on the desert. Together with some friends, Adamski saw the saucer; alone, he located the pilot, who was rather like an Earthman but for that fact that his clothing was rather atypical for a desert expedition. For instance, he was wearing what seemed to be ski trousers. Also he had beautifully waved, shoulder-length hair. He did not talk English, but he was able to indicate that he was a true Venusian, and he appeared to be friendly. At the end of the interview the saucer itself came along, and hovered just above the ground. It was in this remarkable craft that the visitor made his exit.

When the book appeared, it became an immediate bestseller, and George Adamski became famous almost overnight. Other books followed, and in one of them Adamski related how he had been taken up in a saucer and treated to a lunar voyage. I quote: 'As I studied the magnified surface of the Moon, a small animal ran across the area I was observing. I could see that it was four-legged and furry, but its speed prevented me from identifying it.' By this time his hosts had decided to speak English rather than use semaphore, which made things a great deal easier. Eventually the visitors departed for home, but not before Adamski had been the guest of honour at a farewell banquet held in a huge saucer built on the planet Saturn...

All this was great fun, but before long flying saucer societies were founded, and what had been purely a joke turned quite rapidly into a cult which was taken quite seriously. Even the United States Air Force became interested, and set up an organisation to check whether there could be any basis of reality to the stories. The term 'flying saucer' was dropped, to be replaced by the more dignified Unidentified Flying Object, or UFO for short. Not everyone was impressed, and it is on record that Andrei Gromyko, then the Russian Foreign Minister, suggested that the saucers were due to a Soviet discus thrower who had been practicing for the Olympic Games and had failed to appreciate his true strength. The saddest story involved an American who wrote a book in which he claimed to have been taken for a trip in a UFO piloted by a beautiful lady from Venus. His wife did not appreciate his account. She sued her husband for divorce, cited the lady from Venus – and won. (This, I assure you, is absolutely authentic!)

Inevitably it was suggested that UFOs might pose a threat to mankind, and at one stage there was even a mild panic, confined to the State of Michigan and initiated by a college lecturer, Dr Charles Laughead, who claimed to have been in touch with a mystic and had been converted. There would be floods and earthquakes following a new visitation by UFOs, and only those who were true Believers would be saved from a watery grave. Dr Laughead gave the fateful day as 17 December 1954, and a crowd of people gathered near his home, only mildly reassured by the news that a UFO would land and pick them up from the good doctor's back garden. By that time Laughead had been dismissed from the State College, but even after 17 December had passed without incident he remained convinced that the messages had been genuine; God had intervened to stop the flood at the last moment.

One particularly odd theory involves the Hole in the Pole. It is said that an underground civilization, of Martian origin, exists well below the Earth's crust, and that its inhabitants periodically come out through tunnels, presumably to see what is going on above their heads. They may even be preparing to take us over – one method being to dump pumas in the countryside to act as scouts and report back to their masters, so that if you hear mewing sounds from below your feet you will know that a new spy is about to be dispatched. One strong supporter of the Hole in the Pole theory was a British peer, Lord Clancarty, who in 1995 initiated a solemn UFO debate in the House of Lords. So far as the underground civilization was concerned, Lord Clancarty admitted that 'I haven't been down there myself, but from what I can gather these beings are very advanced.' All of which goes to show that W.S. Gilbert was very much on the right track when he wrote *Iolanthe*.

We have heard cases of people who have mysteriously disappeared, and have, it is claimed, been abducted by aliens. One can even take out insurance to guard against this sort of thing.* Aircraft crashes over what has become known as the Bermuda Triangle have also been mentioned, though cynical ex-flyers such as myself suspect that the accidents have been due merely to poor conditions of visibility or to human error. Neither must we forget the books by Erick von Daniken, who maintains that the Earth was visited in ancient times and that God himself may well have been an astronaut. Moreover, what about the Aetherius Society? It has hundreds of members, and I must mention them here, because they claim that they have on several occasions helped to prevent the world from being destroyed. They have been able to do this because their Founder/President, formerly Mr George King of the Fulham

---

*The longest odds of all seem to have been offered by William Hill, who laid 14 million to 1 against the possibility of a flying saucer piloted by Elvis Presley landing on top of the Loch Ness Monster. This does seem to have been a fairly safe bet.

Road, London, and now the Revd Dr Sir George King of California, is on first-name terms with several important personages, including Aetherius, who lives on Venus but who looks after the Earth; Jesus Christ, who is based on Mars; and Confucius, who has been transferred to Saturn, the most advanced of the planets and also the seat of the Interplanetary Parliament. During one crisis, of which most people (including myself) were blissfully unaware, hostile fishermen from across the Galaxy launched a missile towards us, mainly because the oceans on their own world were drying up and they wanted to make use of ours. The news of the impending attack percolated through to the Interplanetary Parliament, which decided to take action. Aetherius was away at the time, but Dr King was informed, and eventually a Martian-launched thunderbolt blasted the missile out of the sky before it could reach us. Now and then, it is important to organise Spiritual Pushes, and also to charge the tops of mountains with Cosmic Energy to make sure that no unfriendly aliens can penetrate our defences. Most of the UFOs, which may be up to 5,000 miles long, come from either Mars or Venus, while Jupiter is the reception planet of the Solar System, and visitors from outer space have to have their passports stamped there before traveling on. Circling the Earth there are several space stations, including Mars Sector 6, which Dr King has actually visited in his capacity as our representative to the Interplanetary Parliament...

Around 1957 I remember going to a meeting of the Aetherius Society at Caxton Hall, in London. Following the address, given personally by Aetherius by way of Dr King's vocal chords, questions were called for. It was emphasised that Aetherius spoke all terrestrial languages, but when I was ill-natured enough to ask a question in Norwegian it caused bafflement. I then repeated it in

French, but this was no good either, and finally it had to be put into English. What I wanted to know, quite simply, was: Where was Aetherius at the moment? On Venus, or in space? Dr King was unfortunately unable to answer. I was merely told, rather brusquely, that Aetherius' present whereabouts was a secret.

Much later I interviewed a representative of the Society on television. I was particularly interested in the Interplanetary Parliament, which meets on Saturn, the most advanced world in the Solar System. I asked what the Saturnians looked like. I was told that at that stage of evolution a being had gained such status that it could be seen in its entirety – that is to say, an ovoid shape; a great incandescent egg at least forty feet tall. I commented that the Saturnians seemed to be very like balls. The reply was that they were in fact complete balls – a description with which I was bound to agree.

Before leaving what must be called the fringe – Roswell. It was said that in July 1947 a saucer crashed at Roswell, in New Mexico, killing its diminutive crew. Conspiracy Theorists have been in full cry ever since, though it has long since been shown that the crashed vehicle was either a weather balloon or some sort of aircraft sent up by the United States military forces. However, Roswell is accepted as the UFO centre of the world, and does a roaring trade in articles such as T-shirts and plaques …

But on a more serious note, what are the chances of global destruction by alien attack?

Of course the idea is very old, and many stories have been written on the theme, notably Wells's *War of the Worlds*. And though we can expect no advanced life-forms in the Solar System, except on Earth, it would be both vain and illogical to claim that we are alone in the universe. The Sun is one of 100,000 million stars in our Galaxy, and our telescopes are capable of photographing at least 1,000 million galaxies, so that the total number of stars is beyond our comprehension. If planetary systems are common, as seems to be indicated by modern theory, we may expect many Earth-like planets orbiting Sun-like stars. Consider, for instance, the southern star Delta Pavonis, which is easily visible with the naked eye, though it is too far south to be seen from Europe. It is nineteen light-years away, and almost identical with our Sun. There is no reason why it should not be attended by an equivalent of the Earth, and Delta Pavonis is a very run-of-the-mill-star. If conditions there are much the same as here, similar life-forms could well have appeared.

I realise that this view is open to challenge, and that at least one of the world's most eminent astronomers is of the opinion that we are unique. Yet every time we have tried to set ourselves upon a pinnacle, we have been disillusioned. Originally it was believed that the Earth was flat, lying at rest at the centre of the universe. Then, when the Greeks showed that the world is a globe, it was still assumed to retain the central position (though a few thinkers, such as Aristarchus of Samos, disagreed). After the revolution in outlook sparked off by Copernicus in the sixteenth century and concluded by Newton with the publication of his *Principia* in 1687, it was still maintained that the Sun at least was of real importance. Next, the Sun was shown to be a normal dwarf star, and finally, in our own century, came the revelation that our Milky Way galaxy is a normal star system. Today it is even suspected that there are super-clusters of galaxies and that we may be seeing only a fraction of the universe.

Not to put too fine a point on it, we have been taken down not merely one peg, but a great many pegs, and if life appears wherever conditions are suited to it we may assume that intelligent beings are scattered throughout our Galaxy and others. They might not look in the least like us, and I am quite prepared to believe in intelligent astronomers with, say, three legs each and several arms, but they would not truly be what science-fiction writers usually term BEMs or Bug-Eyed Monsters. So far as we can tell, all the material in the universe is made up of the same elements as those we know. When we use spectroscopes to analyse the light coming from remote stars or remote galaxies, we find the familiar substances: hydrogen, carbon, iron and the rest. There is no reason to suppose that other elements exist, and every reason to suppose that they do not. This means that all life-forms, wherever they are found, are built up in essentially the same way as ourselves.

I may be wrong. It is not impossible that there is a fundamental flaw in this reasoning, and that the truth is much more complicated. But when you are presented with a set of facts which is admittedly incomplete, the only course is to interpret them as sensibly as you can. Unless any contrary evidence turns up, it is reasonable to believe that extra-terrestrial life will be of our own type, and that we will find no beings made of pure gold living in airless worlds.

Whether our own natures are typical, I do not know. Frankly I hope not, because we have little reason to be proud of ourselves, as two world wars have shown. I will return to this theme later. Meanwhile, let us remember that civilization as we know it is very young. Ten thousand years ago the world was emerging from its latest Ice Age, and a visiting astronaut would have found very little in the way of technology. A million years ago, any alien who landed on Earth would have discovered no 'intelligence' at all by modern standards. Yet a million years is not long when we recall that the world is well over 4,000 million years old, so that civilization as we know it has developed in an amazingly short period of time. Mechanical transport would have seemed far-fetched to Julius Caesar or King

Canute, and the idea of travelling to the Moon would have been dismissed out of hand. Unfortunately our science has far outstripped our ethics, and I would not claim that in this sense we have made any progress since the time of Ancient Athens.

This is not really a digression, because we are considering the possibility of invasion by an alien race. Certainly we are not yet in a position to attempt direct contact with another planetary system. Rockets would take an impossibly long time to reach even the nearest star; if we are to get in touch with faraway races, we must await some fundamental breakthrough about which we cannot speculate as yet, because we have not the faintest notion where to start. Methods such as teleportation and thought-travel are as far-fetched to us as television would have been a thousand years ago.

Now let me come to the real crux of my argument. Any civilization which has learned how to cross interstellar space, either materially or (more probably) by some other means, must have passed through its crisis period and survived. If it had remained warlike, as we are at the moment, it would have liquidated itself. Consequently, any visitors from outer space will not be hostile, and we will have nothing to fear from them. I cannot agree with those scientists who have publicly proclaimed that to send out radio messages, advertising our presence, is to court disaster. It is always possible that an unfriendly civilization might pick up our transmissions and even interpret them, but this could do no harm. Other beings could reach us only if they were genuinely enlightened, and in such a case we could learn a great deal from them.

There is no proof that aliens have ever visited us; the 'evidence' put forward by Erick von Daniken and others does not stand up to examination, and is really no more credible than George Adamski's Venusians or Mr King's

Interplanetary Parliament. Yet a visitation is not out of the question, and one day it may come. Following the same argument, other races will have no cause to fear us if we ourselves master the secret of interstellar flight, because we will then have progressed far beyond our present dangerous state of mind.

In short, it seems there is no chance that the world will end because of alien attack. There is therefore no need to be alarmed on that score.

And So to Science

Up to now we have been discussing ways in which the world will *not* end. Religion gives no clue; the gravitational pulls of the planets, even when working in unison, cannot affect us; the Moon is set firmly and comfortingly in its orbit; we are unlikely to be hit by a major asteroid or a wandering comet; the stars are too remote to threaten us, and we are in no danger from alien beings or flying saucers. It might be thought, then, that I am setting out to prove that the world is eternal. Not so! It has a limited lifespan ahead of it, so let us now turn to what sober science can tell us.

The most important factor of all is the Sun, which sends us virtually all our light and heat. Without the Sun, our Earth would never have come into existence, and we are entirely dependent upon it; if its luminosity changed by even a few per cent, the results so far as we are concerned would be disastrous. Therefore we have to decide whether the Sun's output is likely to alter in the foreseeable future, and this involves saying something about stellar evolution.

It is certain that the Sun, like all other stars, condensed out of interstellar material contained in a nebula. Nebulae, made up of dust and gas, are common enough; the Great Nebula in Orion, near the Hunter's Belt, is a superb example, and any small telescope will show it well, together with four hot stars in the so-called 'Trapezium', which make the nebula shine. (Were there no suitable stars, the nebulosity would be dark, and would be detectable only by the fact that it would blot out the light of stars beyond. Dark nebulae are also common; look for instance at the 'Coal Sack' in the Southern Cross, or the dark rifts in the Milky Way running through Cygnus, the Swan.) The Orion Nebula is a stellar birthplace. It is over a thousand light-years away, and is of tremendous extent, though the gas in it, mainly hydrogen, is millions of times less dense than the Earth's air. Fresh stars are being produced in the Nebula, and at least two have been caught in the act, since they started to shine only a few decades ago. There are also many stars in the Nebula which are very young and are unstable, so that they vary in brilliancy. Rather confusingly these are known as T Tauri stars, because T Tauri itself, in the adjacent constellation of the Bull, was the first-discovered member of the class. And deep in the Orion Nebula, permanently hidden from us, is the mysterious Becklin-Neugebauer Object, named after its co-discoverers. It seems to be a very young, immensely powerful star, detectable only because it sends out floods of infra-red radiations, which, unlike visible light, can slice through the nebular dust and gas.

According to modern estimates, the Sun was born rather over 5,000 million years ago – not suddenly, but over a long period. Inside a dusty, hydrogen-rich cloud, a chance condensation formed; as it grew, its gravitational pull drew in extra material, and eventually the embryo star became so hot inside that it started to shine. At first it flickered irregularly, as the T Tauri stars do now, but eventually it steadied. By then the planets had been produced, and among these, of course, were the Earth and Venus.

There was a protracted period when the Sun had only

about 70 per cent of its present luminosity. The inner parts of the Solar System were cooler, and since Venus and the Earth are near-twins in size and mass they began to evolve along similar lines. But before long, conditions changed, and the Sun became hotter. Earth, at a respectful 93 million miles, escaped the worst of the blast; Venus did not, and suffered dramatically. The seas boiled and then evaporated; life was extinguished, and as the carbonates in the rocks were driven out Venus developed the thick, carbon dioxide atmosphere which still acts in the manner of a greenhouse, shutting in the Sun's heat and raising the surface temperature to a furnace-like 900°F or so. If this scenario is correct (and very recent evidence does point that way), then Venus must be regarded as a tragic world, where life had no chance to evolve beyond its primitive state before being ruthlessly snuffed out.

Before going on, let me pause to dispose of another end-of-the-world suggestion, this time involving the giant planet Jupiter.

Jupiter and Saturn are much the largest members of the Sun's family; Jupiter could accommodate over 1,000 globes the volume of the Earth. Not so very long ago they were believed to be miniature suns. In a famous book, *Saturn and its System*, written by the English astronomer R.A. Proctor in 1882, we find the following:

> A disturbance in Jupiter, and still more in Saturn, to be recognisable from the Earth, must take place on a scale incomparably greater than that on which any terrestrial disturbances, even the most tremendous earth-throes, have taken place within the knowledge of man. Over a region hundreds of thousands of square miles in extent, the glowing surface of the planet must be torn by subplanetary forces. Vast masses of intensely hot vapour must be poured forth from beneath, and rising to enormous heights, must

either sweep away the enwrapping mantle of cloud which had concealed the disturbed surface, or must itself form into a mass of cloud.

This seemed reasonable enough a century ago, and it was not finally disproved until the 1920s, with a series of brilliant theoretical papers by Sir Harold Jeffreys. Direct measurements showed later that far from being hot, the surfaces of Jupiter and Saturn are extremely cold, so the dwarf-sun theory was ruled out.

Yet inside Saturn, and still more so inside the larger and more massive Jupiter, the temperatures must be high, and the pressures are tremendous. One idea, originating in the Soviet Union, is that Jupiter is still scooping up material from the debris that litters the Solar System, and that its mass is increasing, so that eventually the core will become so hot that nuclear reactions will be triggered off. The planet Jupiter will be transformed into the star Jupiter, and the effects on Earth will be dire. Life will probably be wiped out, and the gravitational disturbances might even suck our hapless world into one of the two suns.

This sounds alarming, but in fact it is absolutely out of the question. For one thing, the amount of fresh material which Jupiter could collect is negligible when compared with the present mass of the planet. Though the present core temperature may be as much as 50,000°C, this is very low as against the critical value of 10 million°C which would be needed to make the change from planet into star.

In some respects the Sun itself must be regarded as variable, because of the famous eleven-year-cycle. The bright solar surface or photosphere, at a temperature of almost 6,000°C, is not blank; on it may be seen darker patches known, rather misleadingly, as sunspots. They are not truly dark, but appear so by contrast with the still brighter background, and they change constantly, so that they are fascinating to watch.* They are not always present; no individual spot or spot-group lasts for more than a few months at most, and smaller spots are often gone in a matter of days or even hours. At times of solar maximum (as in 1968–9, 1979–80 and 1990–1), there are many spot-groups together with flares – violent outbursts emitting streams of electrified particles which cross the 93-million-mile gap to Earth and cascade down into the atmosphere, producing the lovely displays of aurorae or polar lights – whereas at times of minimum there may be many consecutive spotless days. The cycle is by no means perfectly regular, but we may expect the next maximum around 2011.

It used to be thought that there was a definite link between the solar cycle and our weather. Nowadays the association is generally regarded as dubious, but it is certainly worth looking back to see if we can find any longer-term cycle. Records indicate that between 1645 and 1715 there were practically no sunspots at all, so that the cycle was suspended; this is known as the Maunder Minimum, after the English astronomer who drew attention to it ninety years ago. This protracted minimum coincided with what is often termed 'the little ice age', when the Thames froze over frequently, and the climate in Iceland was so severe that there was talk of evacuating the whole island. Similar spotless periods seem to have occurred earlier, though we cannot be nearly so confident about them because the records are fragmentary.

Recently we have heard a great deal about global warming, and it has been claimed that our activities are

* Let me repeat a warning which I have given before on countless occasions; never look directly at the Sun through any telescope or binoculars, even with the addition of a darker filter. Permanent damage to the eye, or even total blindness, is almost certain to result. To observe sunspots, project the Sun's image through the telescope on to a white screen or card held behind the eyepiece. On no account look direct, even for a moment.

sending up so much carbon dioxide into the air that within a few decades the temperature will rise sufficiently to make life here very unpleasant. Global warming has become all the rage, and to question it is Politically Incorrect. Well, we are going through a period of warming, but personally I do not believe that we are responsible in any way. Conditions on the Sun do vary, and there are regular warmer and cooler spells. In my view, the present period of warming would be succeeded in the fairly near future with a period of cooling, so that by the year 2100 the temperature conditions will be much the same as they were in 2000. I may be wrong; time will tell.

There is another interesting fact, too. Theory shows that the Sun ought to emit many of the particles known as neutrinos, which are difficult to study because they have no electrical charge and almost (or quite) zero mass. Experiments indicate that the total neutrino flux is much less than theory expects, so that either our knowledge of the Sun's interior is much less than we used to think, or else the Sun really is behaving in an abnormal manner at the present moment.

If the Sun's output of radiation fell, then so would the temperature of the Earth, and this brings us back to the whole question of Ice Ages. Asteroid impacts may have been responsible, but it seems rather more likely that the basic cause is to be found in the fluctuations of the Sun. These may have occurred in the relatively recent past. The last Ice Age ended a mere 10,000 years ago, by which time Man had become firmly established upon the terrestrial scene. Actually, the Ice Age was not a period of constant cold. There were four chilly spells, interspersed with warmer periods, which are termed interglacials – and we may even now be in the midst of an interglacial, in which case the true Ice Age may not be over yet. In any event, there is no doubt that for some time prior to 8000 BC the general temperature of the world was appreciably lower than it is now. The ice-caps at the poles were much more extensive, and the northern ice-sheet extended down almost as far as modern London. At that time England was joined on to the mainland, and it would have been possible for an Ice-Age sportsman to skate across from, say, Norfolk to Norway.

We know much less about conditions in the Antarctic, because there are no continents near the South Pole apart from Antarctica itself, which is still ice-covered and which has no human population apart from the scientists who work at the various research bases. Otherwise, Antarctica is left to penguins and other amiable creatures, who are not in the least worried about the end of the world or, indeed, about anything except finding enough fish to eat for dinner. But the evidence now indicates that during the Ice Age the south, too, was colder than at present, in which case the drop in temperature affected the whole world. This means that Ice Ages can hardly have been due to a shift in the direction of the Earth's axis, which was a favoured theory at one time. If the poles shifted, then admittedly some parts of the world would have been chilled, but others would have become correspondingly warmer.

However, there are some people today who are very worried about the possibility of such a shift, and there is a fully-fledged Pole Watchers Society, which is keeping alert for any sign of danger.

As most people know, the present tilt of the Earth's axis is 23.5 degrees to the perpendicular of its orbit, which is why we have our seasons; during northern summer the north pole is tipped sunwards, while the south pole is inclined in the opposite direction. The fact that the Earth is actually closest to the Sun in December is more or less irrelevant, because the difference is only about 3 million miles, and the effect is masked by the stabilising influence of the great southern oceans. To alter the tilt deliberately would be too much for twentieth-century technology, even if it were wise. There was a famous story by Jules Verne, *The Purchase of the Pole*, in which some experimenters try to change the tilt by using the recoil of a huge cannon, but fail because a careless professor had been making the essential calculations on a blackboard when he fell off his chair, thereby wiping out a vital string of zeros. But the pole watchers of today treat the whole matter very seriously.

I first came across them in 1954, with the publication of a booklet by Adam D. Barber entitled *Disaster Worse than the H-Bomb*. In fact, he was kind enough to send me a personal copy – though I was not singled out; other recipients were Sir Winston Churchill, General de Gaulle, the President of the United States, the Emperor of Japan, and the Pope. Barber was fascinated by gryroscopes, and in particular by the fact that the Earth is wobbling very slowly in the manner of a gyroscope which is about to topple; we have come across this effect earlier, when discussing the astrologers. Barber came to the eventual conclusion that in addition to its orbit round the Sun, the Earth also describes a 'small orbit', so that when the Earth's axis makes a right angle with both the large and small orbits it is liable to slip suddenly by 135 degrees, making the north pole shift by 90 degrees.

To be candid, I have never been able to follow Barber's reasoning, so let me quote from his book:

> The shift is basically caused by gyroscopic processes at right angles to the two orbits of the Earth. This occurs because the Earth itself is a huge gyroscope, and when it reaches the dead centre of its orbits it can no longer press forward. On account of its momentum in its orbit, it creates a gyroscopic pressure at right angles, thereby causing a sudden shift ... The shift will be completed in about one and a half hours.

He went on to say that this shift happens very 9,000 years, the last occasion being (naturally) the time of Noah's Flood, when the seas swept across the lands and produced a global deluge. Finally, he maintained that the danger times were 21 June and 21 December each year, when the Earth 'reaches the extremes of its orbit'.

Barber's book failed to make the impact which he had expected, but, nothing daunted, he continued to make predictions as well as suggest remedies – in particular, fixing powerful jets to the Earth at the two poles, so that firing the motors would stop the shift as soon as it was first noticed! As an extra precaution, he recommended that everyone should build a boat and moor it in a convenient position, so that it could be used immediately the flood-waters arrived. Shades of President Auriol of Toulouse...

In fact there is absolutely no evidence of Barber's 'small orbit', even if you could fathom exactly what it was meant to be, and neither can we have much faith in the theories of another pole-shift enthusiast, Hugh Auchincloss Brown, who died in 1975 at the advanced age of ninety-six. Mr Brown did not believe in Barber-type orbits. Instead, he believed that the weight of the Antarctic ice-cap was increasing so much that it would eventually upset the stability of the entire globe, causing it to topple sideways. In his book *Cataclysms of the Earth*, published in 1967, he forecast that at the next week New York would be submerged thirteen miles below the surface of the ocean. His remedy was to break up the ice-cap with atomic bombs, preventing it from becoming dangerously heavy.

Yet another idea was proposed by Charles Hapgood of the United States, in 1949. This time only the crust of the Earth would slip, gliding over the molten interior, the movement was likely to be very slow, taking thousands of years, and Mr Hapgood was inclined to think that it had already started, so that violent earthquakes might be expected in the future. Finally there is, of course, Dr Velikovsky, whose theories embraced almost every version of eccentricity, and who also included pole shifting in several of his books.

It is true that there are modest fluctuations in the inclination of the axis over a cycle of 41,000 years, so that the tilt ranges between 21.5 degrees and 24.5 degrees, but this is not enough to make a great deal of difference to our climate, and it is certainly too slight and too gradual to worry about. The changes are due to the gravitational pulls of the Sun and Moon, and there is no conceivable mechanism, apart possibly from a really major asteroid collision, which could cause a rapid shift. Incidentally, most of the other planets have axial inclinations much the same as ours, though Jupiter is almost 'upright', Venus spins in the opposite sense to the Earth for some unknown reason, and Uranus is tilted over at an angle of 98 degrees, so that there are times when one pole of the planet is turned directly towards the Sun. The Uranian seasons must be most peculiar; each pole would have a night lasting for twenty-one Earth years, with a corresponding midnight sun at the opposite pole, though it is hardly likely that there are any inhabitants to study it.

No; all these suggested calamities must be discounted. The real, ultimate peril comes from the Sun.

Since the Sun is so hot, it is tempting to suggest that it is burning, in the manner of a coal fire. The surface temperature is almost 6,000°C, which is warm by any standards, and the inner temperature is much higher still. Yet the Sun is too hot to burn; and if it were made up entirely of coal, blazing furiously enough to send out as much heat as the real Sun actually does, it would not last for long before being turned into ashes. Unlike the phoenix, it would be unable to recreate itself, and we must look for a different source of energy. Before going any further I must say something about the spectroscope, which is one of the most important of all astronomical instruments and which many people regard as the most vital of all, though admittedly it does have to be used in conjunction with a powerful telescope.

The initial steps were taken by Isaac Newton in 1666, when Cambridge University was closed because of the Plague, and Newton had temporarily withdrawn to his quiet cottage at Woolsthorpe in Lincolnshire. While there, he began the studies which led him on to the theory of gravitation – and, in passing, the story of the tumbling apple is almost certainly true; he really did see an apple fall, and realised that the force which affected the apple was the same as the force which keeps the Moon moving in its path round the Earth. Newton also made some pioneer experiments with sunlight. He passed a beam of sunlight through a glass prism, and noted that the light was spread out into a succession of colours, from red at one end to violet at the other. This showed him that sunlight is made up of all the colours of the rainbow; the various ingredients are bent differently as they pass through the prism. Blue is bent more than red, yellow less than blue, red less than yellow. That was as far as he went, but he had made the essential breakthrough.

We know, as Newton did not, that light may be regarded as a wave motion, and that the colour of the light depends upon its wavelength, i.e. the distance between successive wave crests. Violet has the shortest wavelength, and is therefore the most strongly bent or refracted as it passes through the prism; red has the longest wavelength, and is refracted the least. By conventional standards, these wavelengths are very tiny. That of red light is about 7,500 Angstroms, while violet goes down to 3,900 Angstroms – and one Angstrom is equal to one hundredth millionth of a centimetre.* Imagine a line exactly one centimetre long. Try mentally to divide it into 100 million parts, and you will appreciate how small an Angstrom is. To the short-wave end of visible light we have ultraviolet, X-rays and the very penetrating gamma rays; beyond the red we have infrared and then radio waves. Most people know at least something about these invisible radiations. If you switch on an electric fire, you will feel the infrared as heat well before the bars start to glow, while X-rays are used every minute in hospitals. Radio waves also come to us from space, though they certainly are not artificial transmissions. All in all, the total range of wavelengths, or 'electromagnetic spectrum', is very extensive.

Matter – all matter: you, me, the Earth, the Sun, the stars and the galaxies – is made up of atoms, which band together to make up atom-groups or molecules. To describe an atom is by no means easy, and in everyday language it simply cannot be done, but I can try to give a general picture. This means repeating a little of what I have said earlier, but atomic studies are so vitally important in any consideration of the Sun's ultimate fate that I make no apology.

To recapitulate, then: in an atom, there is a central nucleus around which revolve particles of lesser mass, rather in the manner of planets moving round the Sun. The nucleus is made up of positively-charged particles (protons) together with particles which have no charge at all (neutrons), while the planetary particles have negative charge (electrons). The nature of the atom depends upon the number of planetary electrons. Thus hydrogen, the simplest and lightest of all the fundamental atom-types or elements, has one electron; helium has two, lithium three,

* The unit is named after the nineteenth-century Swedish physicist Anders Ångström, who carried out a great deal of important work. Typists and printers often bemoan the fact that he was inconvenient enough to have a surname beginning with the Swedish letter Å!

and so on until we reach uranium, which has ninety-two. There is a complete sequence, and we are are sure that no elements have been left out, because one cannot have half an electron. Additional elements, with more than ninety-two electrons, have been made in our laboratories; these include plutonium, which is excessively dangerous and is used, among other things, in the manufacture of nuclear bombs. But all these extra elements are unstable, and they have not been found in nature.

The difficulty about all this is that we cannot picture a proton, an electron or a neutron as a solid lump. However, this is as far as I propose to go at the moment, and I hope that readers with a sound knowledge of physics will not object too strongly to what I realise is a gross over-simplification.

When the light from an incandescent solid, liquid or high-pressure gas is passed through a prism, or something which acts in the same way, the result is a rainbow band or spectrum. When the light from an incandescent low-pressure gas is examined, there is no band; instead, there are disconnected bright lines, and each line is the trademark of some particular element or molecule. Thus if we see two distinctive yellow lines, we know that they are due to the element sodium, and cannot possibly be caused by anything else. All the natural elements may be identified in this way, though some are much more elusive than others.

In 1814 a young German optician named Josef von Fraunhofer examined the spectrum of the Sun, and noted something very curious. There was a rainbow band, as expected, but crossing it there were dark lines, and these lines never changed their positions or their intensities. Fraunhofer mapped them, and they are still often called the Fraunhofer lines (he was not the first to see them, but he pioneered scientific studies of them). More than forty years later two of his countrymen, Kirchhoff and Bunsen, found out how the lines are produced, and so opened up the way to modern solar spectroscopy.

The Sun's surface is made up of shining gas, and emits a rainbow or 'continuous' spectrum. Overlying the bright surface is a region of much thinner gases, and these would normally produce bright or 'emission' lines; but because of the rainbow in the background they are 'reversed', i.e. they appear dark. This does not mean that they cannot be identified. For instance, there are two prominent dark lines in the yellow part of the rainbow which correspond to the famous bright lines emitted by sodium, and so we may be sure that there is sodium in the Sun. By now, over seventy of the ninety-two naturally-occurring elements have been found there.

Of these elements, the most abundant is hydrogen, and indeed the whole universe is rich in hydrogen. In sheer numbers, hydrogen atoms are more plentiful than those of all the other elements put together, and helium comes a poor second. We live, in fact, in a hydrogen-dominated environment, though in our everyday life we are not conscious of it. (Remember, however, that water is made up partly of hydrogen, and the formula H_2O indicates that a water-molecule is composed of two hydrogen atoms together with one atom of oxygen.)

Since the stars are suns, they too would be expected to yield spectra of the same kind – and they do. Things are less easy, because with the Sun there is plenty of light available for analysis, and with the stars we have to collect as much light as possible by using a powerful telescope before passing it through spectroscopic equipment. However, the principles are the same, and in the late nineteenth century some important researches were carried out, notably by an English amateur, William (later Sir William) Huggins and an Italian Jesuit, Angelo Secchi. Their work led on to the first concrete ideas about stellar evolution.

The stars are not alike. With the naked eye it is easy to see that some of them are reddish; Betelgeux in the shoulder of Orion is one example, and Antares in the Scorpion is another, while the brilliant Arcturus in Bootes (the Herdsman), which lies in line with the curve of the Great Bear's tail, is light orange. Vega in Lyra (the Harp or Lyre), which is almost overhead as seen from England during summer evenings, is glorious blue, while Capella in Auriga (the Charioteer), which occupies the overhead position during winter evenings, is yellow like the Sun. In the far south, never visible from anywhere, in Europe, we have the famed Southern Cross, which is compact and brilliant, though its shape is more like that of a kite than an X. Of its leaders, three are bluish-white, while the fourth (Gamma Crucis) is red.

Anyone using binoculars, or a telescope, will be able to make out these colours strongly, and fainter stars also show them. Look, for instance, at Mu Chephei, in the far north of the sky; I am afraid you will have to locate it by means of a star map, because it is only dimly visible without optical aid. Telescopically it is seen to glow deep red which is why Sir William Herschel nicknamed it 'the Garnet Star'.

The different colours indicate differences in surface temperature. This is logical enough; after all, blue heat is hotter than yellow heat, while yellow heat is hotter than orange or red. The very hottest stars have surface temperatures of well over 40,000°C, while others range down to below 30,000°C for Vega, 10,700°C for the pure white Sirius, 6,000°C for the Sun and only about 3,400°C for Betelgeux, while the reddest of all stars are cooler still. Long ago, astronomers began to feel that these various colours indicated some sort of an evolutionary sequence, and then came another revelation which appeared to put matters upon a really firm footing. This was the discovery that red stars, at least, can be divided into two definite classes: giants and dwarfs.

I must here introduce you to what is known as a Hertzsprung-Russell or H-R Diagram, so named because it was worked out by Ejnar Hertzsprung of Denmark and Henry Norris Russell of the United States. They produced a chart in which the stars were plotted according to their spectral types and their luminosities. As you can see on the diagram in the plate section most of the stars fall into a line running from the top left down to the bottom right. This line is called the Main Sequence; the selection of stars given here is absolutely typical, and the Sun itself is a normal Main Sequence star. I have also put in the luminosities, taking the Sun as a standard. At the top of the Main Sequence we have bluish-white stars thousands of times more powerful than the Sun, while at the bottom there are Red Dwarfs, which may be termed cosmic glow-worms. For example, the Red Dwarf star Proxima Centauri, which is actually the closest star to the Solar System at a distance of just over four light-years, has only 0.00006 the luminosity of the Sun, and other known Red Dwarfs are feebler still.

But now look at the red stars! There are some which are real searchlights, and lie to the upper right of the H-R Diagram, making up the giant branch; but red stars about equal in luminosity to the Sun do not exist. The difference between giants and dwarfs is less for orange stars and still less for yellow, after which we come to the hot stars, which are not sharply separated into distinct grades. (For the moment, let us forget about the White Dwarfs, to the lower left of the diagram. They are very much part of the story, but they come into a different category altogether.)

It may be true to say that the H-R Diagrams are about the most significant astronomical charts ever made, and so far as stellar evolution is concerned we would be lost without them. They led at once to a suggested sequence of events which turned out to be wrong, but which seemed to be eminently reasonable at the time. It was thought that a star began its career by condensing out of one of the nebulae, or gas-and-dust clouds, which I have already mentioned. Initially the star was large, cool and therefore red. As it shrank, under the influence of gravity, it became hotter, turning first yellow and then white. When it reached the top of the Main Sequence it would be at the peak of its career, and it would then start to cool off as well as shrinking, becoming in succession a Yellow Dwarf like the Sun, an orange star and then a Red Dwarf, reaching the lower right of the Main Sequence. Finally it would become so cool that it would fade out, ending up as a cold, dead Black Dwarf.

If this picture had been right, then life on Earth would have come to a slow but unpleasant end. As the Sun is now a Yellow Dwarf, it would have passed its peak, and would be slowly cooling down as it shrank. Admittedly the decline would be gradual, but eventually it would make itself felt in no uncertain fashion. The Earth's temperature would fall. The ice-caps at the poles would creep slowly but remorselessly towards the equator; country after country would be covered; and unless some remedy could be found, the habitable parts of the globe would become smaller and smaller until Mankind, or what was left of it, had been forced back to huddle near the equator. Even this would be no more than a temporary respite. As the Sun entered its Red Dwarf phase, the oceans would freeze solid; bitter winds would sweep across the whole world – until at last the temperature became so low that the air itself would turn into first a liquid and then a solid block. By that time no trace of life would be left anywhere on the Earth's surface, and whether the remnants of humanity could survive for long by burrowing underground seems rather improbable. At any rate, the final extinction of life would come well before the last of the Sun's energy sputtered out. All that would be left of the Solar System would be a dark dead star still orbited by the ghosts of its planets.

Death by creeping cold is not an attractive prospect. However, it will not happen, because modern research has shown that the whole scenario is wrong. The Sun is not cooling down as it ages. We will be destroyed not by being frozen, but by being vaporised.

What set astronomers on the right track was that the whole timescale of stellar evolution was wrong. If a star evolved in the manner originally supposed, it would be short-lived; yet we know that the Sun is well over 4,000 million years old, and this meant that some other source of energy had to be found. It was next proposed that the star actually annihilated its material, so that it could draw upon the vast reserves locked up inside its atoms. This swung the timescale too far in the opposite direction. Annihilation could, it was thought, maintain a star for about 10 million years, which did not agree at all with what we had found about the ages of the Sun and the Earth. Then, in 1939, the vital clue was found, mainly by a German-born astronomer named Hans Bethe, who was living in America. He attended a conference in Washington, and on the train journey back to Harvard he started 'doodling' on a piece of paper. Before dinner was served, he had worked out the nuclear reactions which can explain most, if not all, of the difficulties.

Again hydrogen is the key. Normal stars, such as the Sun, use it as 'fuel'. The whole process is very complicated, but I do not propose to fog the issue here, so once again I am going to plead guilty to over-simplification, and consider what happens to various types of stars. The entire life-story depends upon the star's initial mass.

Case 1: *stars of very low mass, less than about one-tenth that of the Sun.* After the star has been formed from the nebular material, it starts to contract and heat up inside; but it is so lightweight that the core temperature never becomes high enough for nuclear reactions to begin. Therefore the star does not achieve anything but faint red luminosity, and though it may shine for a long period it then subsides meekly into the Black Dwarf condition.

Case 2: *stars of mass comparable with that of the Sun.* Here we have a very different picture. As the young star shrinks, it starts to shine – jerkily, so that there is considerable irregular variation; this is, of course, the T Tauri condition mentioned earlier. Then, as the core goes on heating up, it reaches the critical value of about 10 million°C, and nuclear reactions are triggered off. Broadly speaking, the hydrogen nuclei start to run together to make up nuclei of Element No. 2, helium. It takes four hydrogen nuclei to make one helium nucleus, and in the process a little energy is set free and a little mass is lost. It is this energy which keeps the star radiating. With the Sun the loss of mass is equal to 4 million tons per second, and the 'weight' of the Sun is much less now than it was when you started to read this page. (Please do not worry; there is plenty left!) The temperature at the star's core rises to around 15 million°C and the star joins the Main Sequence.

This stage in the lifetime of a solar-mass star is very prolonged. The Sun has been on the Main Sequence for over 4,000 million years, and it has at least an equal time in the future, but eventually the supply of available hydrogen will run low, and the Sun will have to rearrange itself. The outer layers will expand and cool, while the core will shrink and heat up. At this stage different reactions are triggered off; helium reacts, and by a whole series of processes heavier and heavier elements are built up. The Sun will leave the Main Sequence, and enter the giant branch of the H-R Diagram.

This will be fatal to the Earth. In about 3,000 million years the temperature here will become unbearable from our point of view, and in 3,500 million years the heat will be so intense that our oceans will boil away. The Sun will be a Red Giant, with a core temperature of the order of

100 million°C; the diameter will be perhaps 8 million miles. Even this is not final. Eventually the Sun will swell out as far as the present orbit of Mercury, and the luminosity will be more than 2,000 times as great as it is at the present time. Venus certainly, and the Earth probably, will be vaporised.

The Red Giant stage will be relatively brief. As the Sun evolves, it will throw off its outer layers, creating what is termed a planetary nebula – a misleading term, because an object of this sort is not truly a nebula, and has nothing whatever to do with a planet. The thrown-off shell will expand and escape into space, while what is left of the Sun will collapse. It will become very small and incredibly dense, because its constituent nuclei will be crushed together with hardly any waste of space. The Sun will become a White Dwarf.

You can see now why I put White Dwarfs into a special category. They are bankrupt, and nothing lies ahead of them but death, though they can continue shining very feebly for thousands of millions of years before they lose the last of their light and heat. Their densities may reach 200,000 times that of water, so that a thimbleful of White Dwarf material would weigh tons. The best-known White Dwarf is the companion of the brilliant Sirius; it is 26,000 miles in diameter, smaller than a planet such as Uranus or Neptune, but its mass is about the same as that of the Sun. Other even more extreme examples are known, some of them smaller than the Moon.

I hope you will now appreciate why I have taken so long to come to the point! The Earth cannot survive the Sun's Red Giant stage, and this will be the way in which our world really will perish, but for the moment let us complete the story by describing the remaining categories.

Case 3: *stars considerably more massive than the Sun*. With a mass more than 1.4 times that of the Sun, everything is accelerated. As before, we have the contraction stage, a highly-luminous Main Sequence stage and a Red Giant (or super-giant) stage, but the timescale is much shorter than with a mild star such as the Sun, and instead of staying at its peak for thousands of millions of years it may run through its reserves in less than a million years. Consider a star such as S Doradus, which lies in the southern star-system known as the Large Cloud of Magellan. Its luminosity is approximately a million times that of the Sun; it is squandering its 'fuel' at a furious rate, and on the cosmical scale disaster lies close ahead. Eta Carinae, referred to earlier, is in even greater danger. When the collapse starts, things become 'out of control', so to speak, and the star explodes in a cataclysmic outburst; it becomes a supernova. The explosion is fatal. Much of the star's material is blown away, and the remnant sinks down into a tiny, super-dense object made of neutrons – produced when the protons and electrons are forced together, so that their electrical charges cancel each other out. $(+ 1 - 1 = 0.)$ A neutron star is indeed a fascinating object. The diameter may be no more than a few miles, but the density rises to 100 million million times that of water.

The story of the discovery of neutron stars is of such interest that I cannot refrain from saying something about it here, even though since the Sun is not massive enough to form a neutron star, it is rather outside our main theme. In 1967 astronomers at Cambridge University were studying radio waves from space which, as we have seen, are electromagnetic vibrations of long wavelength. A member of the team, Jocelyn Bell (now Dr Jocelyn Bell-Burnell), detected a discrete radio source which was fluctuating so rapidly, and so regularly, that for a short, hectic period it was even thought that the signals might be artificial. Finally, it was decided that the source was a rapidly-rotating neutron star or 'pulsar', associated with an amazingly strong magnetic field.

Other pulsar discoveries followed, and one was found inside the Crab Nebula which, as we have seen, is the wreck of the 1054 supernova. Subsequently the Crab pulsar was identified with a very faint optical object, flashing thirty times every second. This was the first pulsar to be seen visually, and even now there are not many others; most are identified only by their radio signals.

To account for the quick-fire 'flashes', it has been found that the radio energy is being sent out in preferential directions; the magnetic pole of the pulsar is not coincident with the pole of rotation. Each time the Earth passes through the beam, we pick up a pulse of energy (and with the Crab and a few others, an optical flash as well). The effect may be likened to that of a rotating lighthouse beam.

It has also been found that pulsars are definitely gradually slowing down, so that they are losing their energy. The Crab is a good example; it seems that the period will double in about 1,200 years from now. In the long run all pulsars will lose their energy, and we will be left with super-dense, super-massive corpses.

Case 4: *stars of still higher mass*. Here we enter the realms of speculation and uncertainty, and I will be brief, because we are even further removed from the fate of the Sun and the Earth. When the grand collapse starts, gravitation takes over, and no supernova outburst has the chance to happen. The star goes on getting smaller and smaller, denser and denser. As it does so, its escape velocity increases. When even light can no longer break free, it becomes a Black Hole. I have mentioned Black Holes before, in connection with the suggestion that there may be one wandering in the outskirts of the Solar System, but generally our only hope of detecting them is to see how they affect visible objects near them. Probably the best case is that of Cygnus X-1, which consists of a massive star attended by an invisible companion with a mass fifteen times that of the Sun, well into the Black Hole, it is violently heated, and emits X-rays of very short wavelength – hence the designation Cygnus X-1.

Now let us sum matters up, and see what we can find out with regard to the eventual fate of the Earth.

All the researches carried out during the past few decades lead us to believe that our ideas about the past and future of the Sun are more or less correct. We may be wrong in detail but not, I think, about the basic principles: birth by contraction from interstellar material, the start of nuclear reactions, the conversion from hydrogen to helium, the Main Sequence period now in progress, the Red Giant stage, collapse to a White Dwarf, and final death as a cold, dead globe. There is absolutely no fear of a supernova outburst, because the Sun is not nearly massive enough, and even less chance of a collapse into a Black Hole.

Even while the Sun remains on the Main Sequence there may be definite changes. The Sun may well be the cause of the Ice Ages, and it is perfectly capable of causing another; a comparatively slight change in solar output could have devastating results, and mankind would be hard pressed to cope with them. If the temperature dropped to the level of the period before 8000 BC we would certainly survive, though the world population would be reduced. If the climate became markedly warmer, then again we would manage, though it might mean abandoning the equatorial regions and migrating towards the poles. All this, of course, is little more than guesswork, and there is no evidence that any alteration is imminent. In any case, life would persist, always assuming that there were no complicating factors.

Since we have ruled out the possibility of the Sun turning into a nova, we are left with its eventual transformation into a Red Giant. This not only may happen; it will happen. How humanity will react is something we cannot foresee. If we have survived as a race, and put away our atom bombs, there is always the chance that we will have learned enough to achieve interstellar travel, in which event the obvious course would be mass emigration to a planet moving round a more accommodating star. When the Sun swells out, there can be no hope for the innermost planets, Mercury and Venus, and very little for the Earth. At best, our oceans will boil away, the atmosphere will be driven off, and the end product will be a scorched, barren, airless and lifeless globe. It is much more likely that the Earth will be vaporised altogether. There is no hope of migrating to Titan or one of the other satellites of the giant planets; only Titan has a dense atmosphere – and when the Sun heats up, Titan's atmosphere will be driven off.

Three thousand million years is a long time, bearing in mind that what we call modern civilization has not yet lasted for as long as 5,000 years. Moreover, there will be plenty of warning. Assuming that we have continued to progress and prosper, astronomers will start to see the danger signals at an early stage. There will be thousands of years to prepare, and perhaps as long as several millions. Flight from the Earth? Methods of driving the world into a new orbit, further from the Sun and therefore beyond the danger-zone? Some way of modifying the Earth itself, so that we can dispense with the energy sent out by the Sun? This is sheer fantasy, but it is inevitable that the period of intense heat will be succeeded by one of numbing cold.

I do not think that we can profitably pursue the subject any further, because we have so little to guide us, but at least we have decided upon the real fate of the Earth. Life here will not be slowly frozen as the Sun fades, as used to be thought. The end will come by a steady increase of heat, until our present gentle, yellow Sun becomes a sinister red agent of destruction.

At least we have the satisfaction of knowing that you and I won't be there.

Aftermath

There are two vital questions which remain to be answered. We know that the Earth must die eventually, but does this mean that all life in the universe will become extinct? Secondly, will the universe itself come to an end?

Up to now I have been talking mainly about the Solar System, that cosmic village which is ruled by the Sun and of which the Earth is a minor though unique member. The Solar System is contained in the Galaxy, a vast assemblage of around 100,000 million stars, some of which are much older than others; star formation is still going on in nebulae such as that in Orion's Sword. There is a great deal of interstellar material which has not yet been used up, so that the Galaxy is still in its prime.

Before the 1920s it was generally believed that our Galaxy was the only one, but there were doubts about it, and these had been expressed by Sir William Herschel much earlier. Not all the so-called nebulae are of the same type as Orion's Sword. Others give every impression of being made up of stars, and in 1845 that amazing amateur, the Earl of Rosse, completed a telescope powerful enough to show that some of these objects are spiral. For instance, the so-called Whirlpool, in the little constellation of the Hunting Dogs, lives up to its name. The brightest of the 'starry nebulae' visible from Europe is also a spiral, though it is placed at an awkward angle to us and the full beauty is lost. It lies in the constellation of Andromeda, and is just visible with the naked eye as a misty blur. It is known officially as M31, because it was the thirty-first object in a catalogue of star-clusters and nebulae drawn up by Charles Messier, a French contemporary of Herschel's.

Herschel made the vague suggestion that M31 and others of its kind might be separate galaxies – independent 'star cities', lying far beyond the confines of our own. He was quite unable to give any proof (remember, in his day no star distance had been measured), and he kept a completely open mind, but it was a bold guess. Subsequently it was more or less discredited, and was dismissed as a half-forgotten speculation, but it came to the fore again following some outstanding work by an American woman astronomer, Henrietta Leavitt, just before the First World War.

In the far south of the sky there are two objects known as the Magellanic Clouds, or Clouds of Magellan, because they were described by the Portuguese explorer Ferdinand Magellan during his round-the-world voyage, which began in 1519. Actually they must have been seen much earlier than that, because they are easily visible with the naked eye, and to the casual onlooker they resemble broken-off parts of the Milky Way; but it was always obvious that they were something special, and when astronomical photography became a powerful means of investigation they were carefully studied. At Harvard, in the United States, Miss Leavitt took a long, hard look at the pictures of them which had been sent to her from Harvard Observatory's southern station in Peru. In the Clouds she detected some stars which did not shine steadily as most stars do; they brightened and faded over short periods of a few days, and they were completely regular in their behaviour. Variable stars of this kind were already known in our Galaxy, and were called Cepheids, because the best-known member of the class is Delta Cephei.

Miss Leavitt found that the Cepheids with the longer periods – that is to say, those which took a greater time to pass from one maximum to the next – looked more brilliant than those with shorter periods. Now, since the Clouds are so far away, all the stars in them can be regarded as equally distant. The rule of 'the brighter, the slower' held good for all the Cepheids in the Small Magellanic Cloud upon which Miss Leavitt concentrated, and this was of tremendous importance, because it followed that the Cepheids which looked the brighter were genuinely the more luminous. The same rule was valid for the Cepheids in other parts of the sky, some of which, including Delta Cephei itself, are easily visible with the naked eye.

If it is possible to find the real luminosity of a Cepheid merely by following its changes in brightness, we have an immediate clue to its distance. Take two Cepheids, one with a period of five days and the other with a period of seven days. If they look equally brilliant, then the seven-day star must be the further away, because it is the more powerful (I am here ignoring complications such as the dimming of light by interstellar dust). Cepheids could be used as 'standard candles' in space, and because they are highly luminous they can be seen across vast distances.

The problem was taken up by another American, Edwin Hubble, who had the advantage of being able to use what was then the largest telescope in the world: the 100-inch reflector at Mount Wilson in California, completed in 1917. Hubble took photographs of M31 and other spirals, and found Cepheids in them. He could then determine the periods of the Cepheids, find their distances, and hence the distances of the spirals in which they lay. All doubts were banished: the 'starry nebulae' were so remote that they could not possibly be members of our Galaxy. Herschel's hesitant guess had been proved right after all.

M31 is now known to be 2,200,000 light-years away.* The Clouds of Magellan are closer, at less than 200,000 light-years, and there are other galaxies making up what we call the Local Group. Not all are spiral; some are elliptical, and some have no definite shape at all, but all seem to be of the same basic nature. M31 is the senior member of the Local Group, and is larger than our Galaxy, with at least 150,000 million stars. But even this was only a beginning; most of the galaxies were far outside the Local Group, at distances of many millions of light-years.

The Cepheids can extend our surveys out to over 40 million light-years, but then they are lost in the general background glow, and other methods have to take over. In the meantime, another remarkable discovery had been made. Excluding the members of the Local Group, all the galaxies are moving away from us, and the further away they are the faster they go. In fact, the whole universe is expanding.

The clue here was given by the spectroscope. I hope you remember how a star's spectrum is formed; there is a rainbow background, crossed by dark lines characteristic of individual atoms or molecules. Galaxies show spectra made up of the combined light of millions of stars, and they are bound to be something of a jumble, but the main lines can be identified, and they were found to be shifted away from

---

* This is further than Hubble's original estimate of less than a million light-years. In 1952 the German astronomer Walter Baade, working with the Palomar 200-inch reflector, found that there had been an error in the Cepheid scale, and that the universe was larger than had been believed – a trifling error of approximately 100 per cent!

their normal positions. This was explained as being due to the Doppler effect, so named in honour of the Austrian physicist Christian Doppler, who first drew attention to it as long ago as 1842. If a light source is receding, all the lines in the spectrum are moved over towards the longwave or red end of the rainbow band. This is the celebrated Red Shift; and the amount of the Red Shift gives a key to the velocity of recession.

Photographs of the spectra of galaxies left little room for doubt; and though many attempts have been made to explain the Red Shifts in some alternative way, no other explanation has been successful. According to all the current evidence, the expansion of the universe is real. There is a well-defined law (Hubble's Law) which links distance with recessional velocity, and this can be used to extend our measurements still further. Once we know the amount of Red Shift, we can estimate how fast that particular galaxy is racing away, and hence we can obtain its distance. By now we have reached out to thousands of millions of light-years, involving recessional velocities which are almost incredibly great.

Radio telescopes also come into the story, because the Doppler shifts affect radio waves too. Since 1963 much has been heard of 'quasars', which seem to be much smaller than normal galaxies but also much more luminous and remote. ('Quasar' is a convenient abbreviation for 'quasi-stellar' radio source; note that there is no connection between a quasar, which is far outside our Galaxy, and a pulsar, which is comparatively local even though one has recently been discovered in the Large Cloud of Magellan.) If the Red Shifts are not misleading us, then some of the quasars are the most remote objects known to us. Today, images obtained with the Hubble Space Telescope and with the Very Large Telescope at Cerro Paranal, and in the Atacama Desert of Northern Chile, show galaxies and quasars which are more than 12,000 million light-years away, and are receding at over 90 per cent of the speed of light.★

If Hubble's Law remains valid at still greater distances, we will eventually come to a point at which a galaxy (or a quasar) is speeding away at the full velocity of light. In this case we will be unable to see it, and we will have reached the edge of the observable universe, though not necessarily the limit of the universe itself. According to recent estimates, the critical distance may be around 15,000 million light-years, though different authorities have rather different ideas about it.

We can also calculate in reverse, so to speak. Assuming that the explanation has always been at the same rate as it is now, we can estimate that it must have begun 15,000 million years ago, in which case the universe is approximately three times as old as the Earth. But how did the universe come into being? And more importantly still in our present context, how will it end?

The favoured theory at the present time is known commonly as the Big Bang. This assumes that all the matter in the universe came into being at one definite moment in time, in the form of a 'primeval atom'; this primeval atom exploded, so that material spread outwards to form galaxies, then stars and then, in many cases, planetary systems. The expansion will continue indefinitely, so that in the long run each group of galaxies

★ Or so most astronomers think. There are, however, some dissenters, notably Dr Halton Arp, formerly of the Mount Wilson Observatory and now working in Germany, and Sir Fred Hoyle. Arp gives plausible reasons for believing that there is a major error in all our distance measurements beyond our Local Group of galaxies, and that the quasars are not nearly so remote as is conventionally believed. This is a most unpopular theory, because if Arp is right it follows that many PhD theses have to be consigned to the dustbin. For the moment I am going to assume that the Conventional theory is accurate, even though I have personally an inner feeling that Arp is right!

will lose contact with each other group. Stars will die; others will be reborn from the remaining interstellar matter; but this cannot go on for ever, and the end product is a totally cold, dead, dark universe.

A noble but, alas, unsuccessful challenge to the Big Bang was made in the late 1940s by two astronomers at Cambridge University, Thomas Gold and Herman Bondi, who proposed an entirely new theory in which the universe has always existed, and will exist for eternity. As old galaxies vanish over the observable limit, they will be replaced by new ones formed from matter which is created spontaneously out of nothingness. Of course the rate of creation must be much too slow to be detectable, but there is plenty of room, so that from this point of view the theory cannot be attacked, but unfortunately is has been found to have so many other flaws that almost all astronomers have now consigned it to the scientific scrapheap. Rather later came the oscillating or cyclic universe, which I irreverently term the concertina universe. If it is correct, the present phase of expansion will not be permanent, and after a while the galaxies will start to draw together again, finally meeting up to produce another Big Bang. It has been suggested that the interval between successive bangs is of the order of 80,000 million years.

This theory depends upon the average density of material spread through the universe. If the destiny is above a certain critical value, there will be enough gravitational pull to tug the flying galaxies back before they can escape; if the density is too low, this cannot happen, and we are back to the original 'evolutionary' picture.

There is absolutely no doubt that the amount of visible matter – making up the galaxies, the nebulae, the stars, the planets, you and me – is hopelessly inadequate to halt the expansion. But the ways in which the various bodies move indicates that there is a tremendous amount of 'dark' matter, which we cannot see at all. It has even been suggested that visible material makes up no more than around 10 per cent of the whole, so that most of the universe is not seen at all. But what exactly is this 'dark matter'? Can it be due to myriads of low-mass stars, or to material locked up in Black Holes, or to what is termed non-baryonic matter, which is so unlike anything in our experience that we are unable to detect or to recognise it? There are also the mysterious particles termed neutrinos, which have no electrical charge and are thought to have no mass. If a neutrino possesses even a tiny amount of mass, then the universe might be 'closed'. At the moment we have to concede that we simply do not know.

Another novel idea has been put forward by the eminent Swedish scientist Hannes Alfven, who has suggested that there may be whole galaxies which are made up of matter of a type fundamentally opposite to our own, so that a collision between anti-matter and ordinary matter would mean the instant annihilation of both. This is not impossible, but we have to admit that the evidence is nil, and the concept remains nothing more than fascinating speculation.

All this is very interesting, but I suggest that we are merely seeking round the basic problem. Just how did the material making up the universe come into existence in the first place? This is a question which nobody (except the Biblical Fundamentalists) has attempted to answer, and neither are we any better off when we consider the timescale. If the universe began at a set moment, what happened before that? Yet if we follow the cyclic picture, and assume that there have been many Big Bangs in the past, we are faced with the problem of understanding a period of time that had no beginning. Our brains are unequal to the task, and the question itself may be regarded as unfair. It is four-dimensional, and we are three-dimensional beings – which is another way of saying that I have no clue as to the answer!

Therefore, what we are discussing is not the origin of the universe, but its evolution, which is a different thing. Moreover, how big is space? It may be 'infinite but unbounded', though to put this into everyday language defeats me, and has, I claim, defeated every other writer as well.

I have called this chapter 'Aftermath', and surely we are entitled to speculate about what will happen after the end of the Earth. Will our remote descendants succeed in emigrating? If so, they will make a new home on some other planet of some other star; but this star also must die eventually, so that there will have to be a further move. We can even let our imaginations run riot, and visualize intelligent beings travelling desperately from one dying system to another until they are faced with the stark realisation that the universe itself has reached its last stages. Yet can there be any chance of a reprieve in some manner quite beyond our understanding? It must be possible, but we have no present hope of finding out.

2010

And so we approach the second decade of the new millennium. What does it hold in store for us – and is there any chance that the world will come to an end before the next thousand years have run their course?

The only tangible cosmic threat comes from asteroids or comets. The dangers of collision are very low, but they are not nil, and it is idle to pretend that they are. Bear in mind, however, that even a major impact would not destroy the Earth itself, or even knock it out of its orbit round the Sun. It might wipe out life here, but that is not the same thing (though from our point of view it would not make much difference).

Frankly, the greatest danger to mankind comes from ourselves. Nuclear bombs now exist which would make those dropped on Hiroshima and Nagasaki look like squibs. Yet even if all the bombs now stockpiled were exploded at once, the jolt would still be too slight to disrupt the Earth completely. However, the crust might well be broken, resulting in major earthquakes and colossal outpourings of lava; tidal waves would devastate the lands, and the atmosphere would become strongly radioactive. The Earth would survive, but life upon it would not.

Everything depends upon politics, and I have to admit that looking round at the present world leaders inspires me with a feeling of no confidence at all. It is hopelessly naïve to suggest that any future war between the great nations will be fought without the use of atomic weapons; of course this would not be so – because nuclear power would be used eventually by whichever side happened to be losing. The present crisis will last for perhaps five hundred years yet. I am always mindful of a comment made as long ago as 1907 by Percival Lowell, founder of the observatory in Arizona. He wrote: 'War is a survival among us from savage times, and affects now chiefly the boyish and unthinking element of the nation. The wisest realise that there are better ways for practicing heroism and other and more certain ends of ensuring the survival of the fittest. It is something a people outgrow.' With this, few sane people would disagree.

It is conceivable that the same situation may have prevailed on other planets, far beyond the Solar Systems. A civilization may well develop the power to destroy itself before it acquires the wisdom not to do so. In our Galaxy alone there must surely be many worlds where civilization is just beginning; worlds where civilization has flourished, and is now far ahead of ours; and also wrecked, radioactive worlds where civilization has died. But this is no place to plunge into the murky realm of politics, so let us come back to the new millennium. When did it start, and who was the first to greet it?

Defying all logic, most people opted for 1 January 2000. Among these were the brilliant statesmen of the British Government. When No. 10 Downing Street announced that 31 December 1999 would be a public holiday, in preparation for dawn on the following day, a pungent comment was made by an Australian MP: 'Common sense tells you that you can't count a year until the year is up. A cricketer doesn't claim a century until he has scored 100 runs.' Of course, taking 1000 as the starting-point will at least mean having two celebration parties instead of one, something which will certainly not be overlooked by commercial interests.

If we accept 1 January 2001, we have next to decide just where the first sunrise was seen. There were fierce arguments about this, and some very dubious tactics were employed – indeed, one might even call them skullduggery!

Have you ever heard of Pitt Island? Possibly not. It is one of the Chatham Islands, around 300 miles south-east of Wellington in New Zealand, and it is the home of forty-five people and several thousand sheep. On it is a modest peak, Hakepa Hill, 750 feet high. At latitude 44 degrees 16 minutes south and longitude 176 degrees 10 minutes west, it has been claimed that the summit of Hakepa Hill was the first inhabited part of the world to see the first sunrise of the new millennium.

Plans for the occasion were laid well in advance. The Millennium Adventure Company took bookings for expeditions there, and claimed that the event would raise 'tens of millions of dollars for the islanders' – and, no doubt, for the company as well. It was expected that there would be a roaring trade in T-shirts, mugs, plaques and souvenirs of all kinds. A contract was signed with the owners of Hakepa Hill, and all seemed well.

However, others soon joined in. A London-based film company, New Dawn 2000(!) pointed out that Hakepa was often mist-shrouded, and they planned a separate party on another hill not far away. The Millennium Adventure Company retaliated by threatening to erect a ten-foot fence on Hakepa, effectively blocking their rivals' view – a procedure which a spokesman for New Dawn 2000 termed 'reprehensible'. It was also pointed out than an even earlier sunrise could be seen from a boat some distance off the island's coast.

Enter the Government of Kiribati. Kiribati* (in case you didn't know) is an independent republic, made up of low-lying atolls divided into three main groups: the Gilbert, Phoenix and Line Islands. The total area is 342 square miles, and some 78,000 people live there. The Republic is crossed by the equator (the capital, Tirwana, lies just in the northern hemisphere). It is said that a visit to the Kiribati Republic is like returning to the Pacific as it used to be half a century ago, and that the locals are friendly and welcoming. The Republic is also crossed by the International Date Line, which divides the world into its eastern and western hemispheres. This is the line which passes through both the Earth's poles, and also through the Old Greenwich Observatory in Outer London. For political reasons it is not uniform, but often bends around to avoid cutting Pacific nations in two. Kiribati was divided. The western area, including Tirawna, was not a mere two hours behind Eastern Kiribati (due to a longitude difference of 30 degrees), but a whole day and two hours behind, which made things decidedly complicated. Therefore, in 1995 Kiribati decided to shift the International Date Line so as to bring the entire nation into the same time zone. Since the Line was established by international agreement, and was not bound by any formal treaties or agreements, nobody minded this, and the rest of the world followed Kiribati's new line.

Yet there were other reasons for the change. It meant that the first sunrise of the new millennium would be over Kiribati rather than New Zealand. It was claimed that priority would go to Caroline Island, actually an atoll of twenty-two islets. It is uninhabited, and is protected by a shallow reef, so that it can be reached only by shallow draft boat or by seaplane. There were even ideas of renaming it Millennium Island.

Of course this was hotly disputed by the Pitt organizers,

* Apparently this is pronounced 'Kiribas'. Please don't ask me why.

who maintained that Kiribati had simply followed the procedure of moving the goalposts midway in a game of football. There were other complications to be taken into account – such as the refraction of light, and local hills and depressions. Moreover, if the skies were cloudy, the 'first sunrise' would not be seen at all.

Finally, let me repeat again that the whole concept of the new millennium is inherently meaningless. It depends upon the Christian calendar, which is accepted by only half the world's population, and if we reckon from the birth of Christ, rather than the official AD 1, the new millennium crept in unnoticed several years ago.

One last word. Over the Antarctic, the Sun never sets in December. Therefore, the first observer of the Sun at the start of the new millennium was neither a watcher from Hakepa Hill, a lone sailor, nor an enthusiast on Caroline Island. It was – a penguin.

I have done my best to present you with a balanced picture. We have looked at the religious fanatics such as William Miller, the astrologers and other eccentrics, the scares due to comets and asteroids. Orson Welles' Martians and Herr Hörbiger's icy Moon; we have entered the fascinating realm of flying saucers, and we have returned to sober science to discuss the eventual death of the Sun. We have allowed ourselves a final look forward to the fate of the universe. And what conclusions can we reach? The Earth itself is in no danger, and will continue in its path until the Sun destroys it, which will not be for thousands of millions of years yet. Life may be wiped out by our own folly, but the Earth will survive.

Make no mistake about it: the world will come to an end one day. But not yet.

Index